Zamaro
Southern Football League
Supporters' Guide
and Yearbook
2011

EDITOR
John Robinson

First Edition

For details of our range of over 1,750 books
and 350 DVDs, visit our web site or contact us
using the information shown below.

British Library Cataloguing in Publication Data
A catalogue record for this book is available from the British Library

ISBN: 978-1-86223-201-3

Copyright © 2010, SOCCER BOOKS LIMITED (01472 696226)
72 St. Peter's Avenue, Cleethorpes, N.E. Lincolnshire, DN35 8HU, England
Web site   http://www.soccer-books.co.uk
e-mail   info@soccer-books.co.uk

Manufactured in the UK by QNS Printing, Newcastle-upon-Tyne, NE6 2XX

FOREWORD

The "Supporters' Guide" series of books began life as "The Travelling Supporters' Guide" in 1982 and a separate guide covering the top two tiers of the Non-League pyramid has been published by Soccer Books Limited for almost 20 years! However, this is the first edition of a Supporters' Guide dealing solely with the Zamaretto Southern Football League clubs and we hope that it is well received.

We have been unable to visit every ground in the course of preparing this guide and, as a consequence, some of the ground photographs are not as up to date as we would have liked. However, we hope to rectify this for future editions and also intend to make this title a regular publication in the Supporters' Guide series.

Where we use the term 'Child' for concessionary prices, this is often also the price charged to Senior Citizens. As the VAT rate will increase in 2011, supporters' should note that this will inevitably result in higher matchday admission prices compared to those shown.

The fixtures listed later in this book were released just a short time before we went to print and, as such, some of the dates shown may be subject to change. We therefore suggest that readers treat these fixtures as a rough guide and check dates carefully before attending matches.

Finally, we would like to wish our readers a safe and happy spectating season.

John Robinson
EDITOR

Note: Bromsgrove Rovers FC were excluded from membership of the League just as this book went to print. As the club has the opportunity to appeal against this decision, we have therefore decided to include a restricted entry for them in this guide.

ACKNOWLEDGEMENTS

In the 6 months since we embarked upon the preparation of this guide, we have been greatly impressed by the cooperation extended to us by League officials and many individuals within the clubs themselves.

Consequently, our thanks go to the numerous club officials who have aided us in the compilation of information contained in this guide and also to Jason Mills of the Zamaretto Southern Football League for his assistance. Our thanks also go to Michael Robinson (page layouts), Bob Budd (cover artwork), Tony Brown (Cup Statistics – www.soccerdata.com) and Dave Twydell and Derek Mead for providing some of the photographs. We would also like to thank:

Chris Bush – footballgroundz.co.uk
David Bauckham – davidbauckham.photoshelter.com
and Martin Wray – www.footballgroundsinfocus.com

for providing some of the other ground photographs used within this guide.

CONTENTS

THE ZAMARETTO LEAGUE PREMIER DIVISION

Secretary Jason Mills

Correspondence
secretary@southern-football-league.co.uk

Web Site www.southern-football-league.co.uk

Clubs for the 2010/2011 Season

BANBURY UNITED FC

Founded: 1931
Former Names: Spencer Villa FC and Banbury Spencer FC
Nickname: 'The Puritans'
Ground: Spencer Stadium, Station Approach, Banbury OX16 5AB
Record Attendance: 7,160 (vs Oxford City – 1948)

Pitch Size: 110 × 70 yards
Colours: Red and Gold shirts with Red shorts
Telephone N°: (01295) 263354
Fax Number: (01295) 276492
Ground Capacity: 4,500
Seating Capacity: 250
Web site: www.banburyunited.co.uk

GENERAL INFORMATION

Car Parking: At the ground
Coach Parking: At the ground
Nearest Railway Station: Banbury (adjacent)
Nearest Bus Station: Banbury
Club Shop: At the ground
Opening Times: Matchdays only
Telephone N°: (01295) 263354

GROUND INFORMATION

Away Supporters' Entrances & Sections:
No usual segregation

ADMISSION INFO (2010/2011 PRICES)

Adult Standing: £8.00
Adult Seating: £8.00
Senior Citizen/Junior Standing: £3.50
Senior Citizen/Junior Seating: £3.50
Programme Price: £1.50

DISABLED INFORMATION

Wheelchairs: 6 spaces available in total
Helpers: Admitted
Prices: Normal prices apply
Disabled Toilets: Available
Contact: (01295) 263354

Travelling Supporters' Information:
Routes: Exit the M40 at Junction 11 and head towards Banbury. Go straight on at the first roundabout then left at the next into Concorde Avenue. Continue straight on at the next roundabout then turn left at the traffic lights. Take the 1st turning on the right into Station Approach then take the single track road on the extreme right of the Station which leads to the Stadium.

BASHLEY FC

Founded: 1947
Former Names: None
Nickname: 'The Bash'
Ground: Bashley Road Ground, Bashley Road, New Milton   BH25   5RY
Record Attendance: 3,500 (1987/88 season)

Colours: Gold shirts with Black shorts
Telephone Nº: (01425) 620280
Ground Capacity: 4,250
Seating Capacity: 250
Web Site: www.bashleyfc.co.uk

GENERAL INFORMATION
Car Parking: Available 100 yards from the ground
Coach Parking: At the ground
Nearest Railway Station: New Milton (1¼ miles)
Club Shop: At the ground
Opening Times: Matchdays only, open one hour before kick-off and also during half-time
Telephone Nº: (01425) 620280

GROUND INFORMATION
Away Supporters' Entrances & Sections:
No usual segregation

ADMISSION INFO (2010/2011 PRICES)
Adult Standing: £10.00
Adult Seating: £12.00
Concessionary Standing/Seating: £8.00
Note: Under-16s are admitted for £2.00 when accompanied by a paying adult
Programme Price: £1.50

DISABLED INFORMATION
Wheelchairs: Accommodated
Helpers: Admitted
Prices: Concessionary prices are charged for the disabled and helpers
Disabled Toilets: None
Contact: (01425) 620280   (Bookings are not necessary)

Travelling Supporters' Information:
Routes: The ground is located by the side of the B3058 in Bashley, just to the north of New Milton. Head southwards on the B3058 towards New Milton, bear right at the Rising Sun Public House and enter Bashley village. The ground is located on the left hand side of the road, shortly after passing the Esso petrol station.

BEDFORD TOWN FC

Founded: 1908 (Re-formed in 1989)
Former Names: None
Nickname: 'Eagles'
Ground: The Eyrie, Meadow Lane, Cardington, Bedford MK44 3SB
Record Attendance: 3,000 (6th August 1993)
Pitch Size: 110 × 72 yards

Colours: Shirts are Blue with White trim, Blue shorts
Telephone N°: (01234) 831558
Fax Number: (01234) 831990
Ground Capacity: 3,000
Seating Capacity: 300
Web site: www.bedfordeagles.net
E-mail: david.swallow@bedfordeagles.net

GENERAL INFORMATION
Car Parking: At the ground
Coach Parking: At the ground
Nearest Railway Station: Bedford Midland (3 miles)
Nearest Bus Station: Greyfriars, Bedford (3 miles)
Club Shop: At the ground
Opening Times: Matchdays only
Telephone N°: (01234) 831558

GROUND INFORMATION
Away Supporters' Entrances & Sections:
No usual segregation

ADMISSION INFO (2010/2011 PRICES)
Adult Standing: £9.00   **Adult Seating:** £10.00
Concessionary Standing: £6.00
Concessionary Seating: £7.00
Children Aged 13 and under Standing: £2.00
Children Aged 13 and under Seating: £3.00
Programme Price: £1.50

DISABLED INFORMATION
Wheelchairs: Accommodated
Helpers: Admitted
Prices: Normal prices apply
Disabled Toilets: Available
Contact: (01234) 831558   (Bookings are not necessary)

Travelling Supporters' Information:
Routes: From the M1: Exit the M1 at Junction 13 onto the A421. Follow this the the bypass at the Sandy exit and take the A603 towards Sandy. The ground is on the left just before the lay-by; From the A1: Take the Sandy exit, go through Willington and the ground is on the right; From Bedford: Follow signs for Sandy and take Cardington Road out of town. The ground is on the left past 2 mini-roundabouts.

BRACKLEY TOWN FC

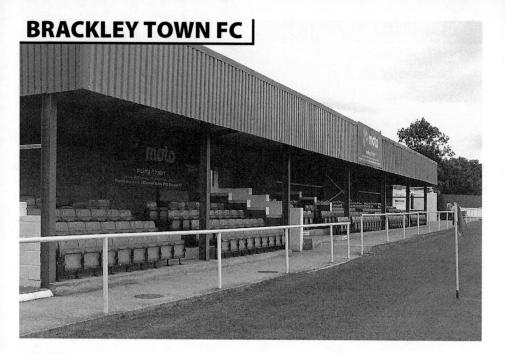

Founded: 1890
Former Names: None
Nickname: 'Saints'
Ground: St. James Park, Churchill Way, Brackley, NN13 7EJ
Record Attendance: 980 (2009/10 season)

Colours: Red and White striped shirts with Red shorts
Telephone Nº: (01280) 704077
Ground Capacity: 3,500
Seating Capacity: 300
Web Site: www.brackleytownfc.com

GENERAL INFORMATION
Car Parking: At the ground (£2.00 charge per car)
Coach Parking: At the ground
Nearest Railway Station: King's Sutton (6¾ miles)
Club Shop: At the ground
Opening Times: Matchdays and by appointment only
Telephone Nº: (01280) 704077

GROUND INFORMATION
Away Supporters' Entrances & Sections:
No usual segregation

ADMISSION INFO (2010/2011 PRICES)
Adult Standing/Seating: £8.00
Senior Citizen/Student Standing: £4.00
Senior Citizen/Student Seating: £4.00
Under-16s Standing/Seating: £2.00
Programme Price: £1.50

DISABLED INFORMATION
Wheelchairs: Accommodated
Helpers: Admitted
Prices: Normal prices apply for the disabled and helpers
Disabled Toilets: Available
Contact: (01280) 704077 (Stephen Toghill – bookings are necessary)

Travelling Supporters' Information:
Routes: From the West: Take the A422 to Brackley and take the first exit at the roundabout with the junction of the A43, heading north into Oxford Road. * Go straight on at the next roundabout and continue into Bridge Street before turning right into Churchill Way. The ground is located at the end of the road; From the South: Take the A43 northwards to Brackley. Take the second exit at the roundabout with the junction of the A422 and head into Oxford Road. Then as from * above; From the North-East: Take the A43 to Brackley. Upon reaching Brackley, take the 1st exit at the 1st roundabout, the 2nd exit at the next roundabout then the 3rd exit at the following roundabout into Oxford Road. Then as from * above.

CAMBRIDGE CITY FC

Founded: 1908
Former Names: Cambridge Town FC
Nickname: 'Lilywhites'
Ground: City Ground, Milton Road, Cambridge, CB4 1UY
Record Attendance: 12,058 (1950)
Pitch Size: 110 × 70 yards

Colours: White shirts with Black shorts
Telephone N°: (01223) 357973
Fax Number: (01223) 351582
Ground Capacity: 2,300   **Seating Capacity:** 523
Correspondence: Andy Dewey, 50 Doggett Road, Cambridge   CB1 9LF
Web site: www.cambridgecityfc.com

GENERAL INFORMATION

Car Parking: 300 spaces available at the ground
Coach Parking: At the ground
Nearest Railway Station: Cambridge (2 miles)
Nearest Bus Station: Cambridge
Club Shop: At the ground
Opening Times: Matchdays only
Telephone N°: (01223) 357973

GROUND INFORMATION

Away Supporters' Entrances & Sections:
No usual segregation

ADMISSION INFO (2010/2011 PRICES)

Adult Standing: £10.00   **Adult Seating:** £10.00
Concessionary Standing/Seating: £5.00
Under-16s Standing/Seating: £2.00
Note: Under-12s are admitted free of charge
Programme Price: £2.00

DISABLED INFORMATION

Wheelchairs: 6 spaces are available under cover on the half-way line
Helpers: Admitted
Prices: One helper admitted free with each disabled fan
Disabled Toilets: Two available in the Main Stand
Contact: (01223) 357973   (Bookings are not necessary)

Travelling Supporters' Information:
Routes: Exit the M11 at Junction 13 and take the A1303 into the City. At the end of Madingley Road, turn left into Chesterton Lane and then Chesterton Road. Go into the one-way system and turn left into Milton Road (A10) and the ground is on the left behind the Westbrook Centre.

CHESHAM UNITED FC

Founded: 1887
Former Names: Chesham Generals FC and Chesham Town FC
Nickname: 'The Generals'
Ground: The Meadow, Amy Lane, Chesham, Buckinghamshire HP5 1NE

Record Attendance: 5,000 (5th December 1979)
Colours: Claret shirts and shorts
Telephone N°: (01494) 783964
Fax Number: (01494) 782456
Ground Capacity: 5,000 **Seating Capacity:** 250
Web site: www.cheshamunited.co.uk

GENERAL INFORMATION
Car Parking: At the ground
Coach Parking: At the ground
Nearest Railway Station: Chesham (½ mile)
Nearest Bus Station: Chesham (10 minutes walk)
Club Shop: At the ground
Opening Times: Matchdays only
Telephone N°: (01494) 783964

GROUND INFORMATION
Away Supporters' Entrances & Sections:
No usual segregation

ADMISSION INFO (2010/2011 PRICES)
Adult Standing: £8.00
Adult Seating: £9.00
Under-16s Standing: £2.00 (Children under 6 free)
Under-16s Seating: £3.00 (Children under 6 free)
Senior Citizen/Student Standing: £5.00
Senior Citizen/Student Seating: £6.00
Programme Price: £1.50

DISABLED INFORMATION
Wheelchairs: Accommodated
Helpers: Admitted
Prices: Normal prices apply
Disabled Toilets: None
Contact: (01494) 783964 (Bookings are not necessary)

Travelling Supporters' Information:
Routes: The ground is situated on the A416. From the M40: Exit at Junction 2 (Beaconsfield) and follow signs to Amersham (A355) and then Chesham (A416). At the foot of the hill before entering town, turn sharp left at the roundabout for the ground; From the M25: Exit at Junction 20 (Abbot's Langley) and follow signs for the A41 (Aylesbury). Leave the A41 at the turn-off for Chesham, pass through Ashley Green until reaching Chesham. Pass through the town following signs for Amersham pass two garages then turn right at the roundabout for the ground; From the M1: Exit at Junction 8, follow signs to Hemel Hempstead then joing the A41 for Aylesbury. Then as above.

CHIPPENHAM TOWN FC

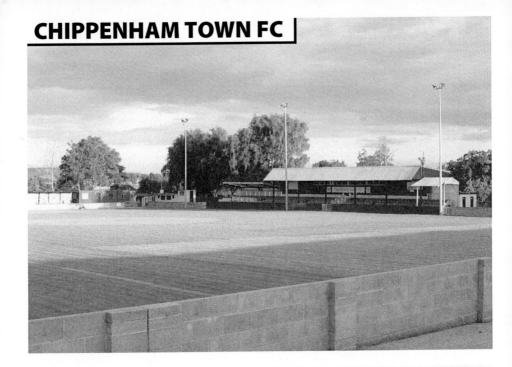

Founded: 1873
Former Names: None
Nickname: 'The Bluebirds'
Ground: Hardenhuish Park, Bristol Road, Chippenham, Wiltshire   SN14 6LR
Record Attendance: 4,800 (1951)
Pitch Size: 110 × 70 yards

Colours: Royal Blue & White shirts, Royal Blue shorts
Telephone Nº: (01249) 650400
Contact Nº: (01249) 815516 (Football Secretary)
Fax Number: (01249) 650400
Ground Capacity: 3,000
Seating Capacity: 276
Web site: www.chippenhamtownfc.com

GENERAL INFORMATION

Car Parking: Adjacent to the ground
Coach Parking: At the ground
Nearest Railway Station: Chippenham (1 mile)
Nearest Bus Station: Chippenham
Club Shop: At the ground
Opening Times: Matchdays only
Telephone Nº: –

GROUND INFORMATION

Away Supporters' Entrances & Sections:
No usual segregation

ADMISSION INFO (2010/2011 PRICES)

Adult Standing: £8.00
Adult Seating: £9.00
Concessionary Standing: £5.00
Concessionary Seating: £6.00
Child Standing: £3.00
Child Seating: £4.00
Programme Price: £2.00

DISABLED INFORMATION

Wheelchairs: Accommodated at front of Stand
Helpers: Admitted
Prices: Normal prices apply for the disabled. Free for helpers
Disabled Toilets: None
Contact: (01249) 650400   (Bookings are not necessary)

Travelling Supporters' Information:
Routes: Exit the M4 at Junction 17 and take the A350. Turn right at the first roundabout and follow the road to the junction with the A420. Turn left following 'Town Centre' signs and the ground is just over ½ mile on the left near the Pelican crossing.

CIRENCESTER TOWN FC

Founded: 1889
Former Names: None
Nickname: 'Centurions'
Ground: Corinium Stadium, Kingshill Lane, Cirencester   GL7 1HS
Record Attendance: 2,600 (vs Fareham – 1969)
Pitch Size: 110 × 70 yards

Colours: Red and Black shirts with Black shorts
Telephone Nº: (01285) 654543
Fax Number: (01285) 654474
Ground Capacity: 4,500
Seating Capacity: 550
Web site: www.cirentownfc.com

GENERAL INFORMATION
Car Parking: At the ground
Coach Parking: At the ground
Nearest Railway Station: Kemble (3 miles)
Nearest Bus Station: Cirencester (1 mile)
Club Shop: None

GROUND INFORMATION
Away Supporters' Entrances & Sections:
No usual segregation

ADMISSION INFO (2010/2011 PRICES)
Adult Standing: £7.00
Adult Seating: £7.00
Senior Citizen/Junior Standing: £4.00
Senior Citizen/Junior Seating: £4.00
Note: It is free of charge for under 5s and Junior Members
Programme Price: £1.50

DISABLED INFORMATION
Wheelchairs: Accommodated
Helpers: Admitted
Prices: Normal prices apply
Disabled Toilets: Available in the Clubhouse
Contact: (01285) 654543

Travelling Supporters' Information:
Routes: Leave the Cirencester Bypass (A46) at the Burford Road roundabout following signs for Stow. Turn right at the traffic lights then right again at the junction. Take the 1st left into Kingshill Lane and the ground is situated about ¼ mile on the right.

DIDCOT TOWN FC

Founded: 1907
Former Names: None
Nickname: 'Railwaymen'
Ground: NPower Loop Meadow Stadium, Bowmont Water, Didcot   OX11 7GA
Record Attendance: 1,512 (2005)

Colours: Red and White shirts with White shorts
Telephone N°: (01235) 813138
Fax Number: (01235) 816352
Ground Capacity: 5,000
Seating Capacity: 250
Web Site: www.didcottownfc.com

GENERAL INFORMATION

Car Parking: At the ground
Coach Parking: At the ground
Nearest Railway Station: Didcot Parkway (5 minute walk)
Club Shop: At the ground
Opening Times: Matchdays only
Telephone N°: –

GROUND INFORMATION

Away Supporters' Entrances & Sections:
No usual segregation

ADMISSION INFO (2010/2011 PRICES)

Adult Standing: £9.00
Adult Seating: £9.00
Concessionary Standing/Seating: £5.00
Under-16s Standing/Seating: £2.00
Programme Price: £2.00

DISABLED INFORMATION

Wheelchairs: Accommodated
Helpers: Admitted
Prices: Normal prices apply for the disabled and helpers
Disabled Toilets: Available
Contact: (01235) 813138   (Bookings are not necessary)

Travelling Supporters' Information:
Routes: From the A34 take the A4130 towards Didcot passing the Power Station on your left. Take the first exit at the first roundabout, the 3rd exit at the next roundabout then go straight on at the next two roundabouts. After crossing the railwayline turn right at the next roundabout into Avon Way. Go over the speed bump go straight over the next roundabout into Bowmont Water. The Ground and car park is on the left.

EVESHAM UNITED FC

Evesham United FC are groundsharing with Worcester City FC until work on their new ground is completed. Please contact the club for further information.

Founded: 1945
Former Names: Evesham Town FC
Nickname: 'The Robins'
Ground: St. Georges Lane, Worcester   WR1 1QT
Record Attendance: –
Pitch Size: 110 × 75 yards

Colours: Red and White striped shirts, White shorts
Telephone Nº: (01905) 23003
Fax Number: (01905) 26668
Ground Capacity: 4,500
Seating Capacity: 1,100
Web site: www.eveshamunitedfc.com

GENERAL INFORMATION
Car Parking: Street parking
Coach Parking: Street parking
Nearest Railway Station: Foregate Street (1 mile)
Nearest Bus Station: Crowngate Bus Station
Club Shop: At the ground
Opening Times: Matchdays only
Telephone Nº: –

GROUND INFORMATION
Away Supporters' Entrances & Sections:
Turnstile at the Canal End when segregation is in force for Canal End accommodation

ADMISSION INFO (2010/2011 PRICES)
Adult Standing: £8.00
Adult Seating: £8.00
Senior Citizen/Junior Standing: £4.00
Senior Citizen/Junior Seating: £4.00
Programme Price: £1.50

DISABLED INFORMATION
Wheelchairs: Accommodated
Helpers: Admitted
Prices: Standard prices apply
Disabled Toilets: Available
Contact: (01684) 561770 (Mike Peplow – Football Secretary)

Travelling Supporters' Information:
Routes: Exit the M5 at Junction 6 and take the A449 Kidderminster Road. Follow to the end of the dual carriageway and take the second exit at the roundabout for Worcester City Centre. At the first set of traffic lights turn right into the town centre. The 3rd turning on the left is St. Georges Lane.

HALESOWEN TOWN FC

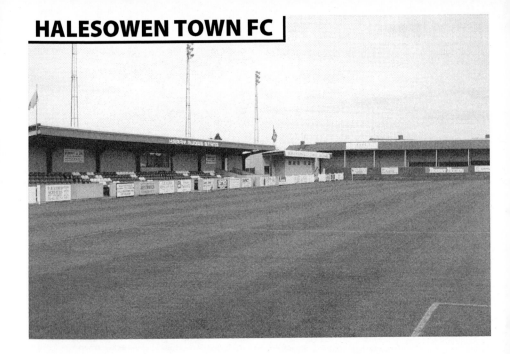

Founded: 1873
Former Names: None
Nickname: 'The Yeltz'
Ground: The Grove, Old Hawne Lane, Halesowen, West Midlands   B63 3TB
Record Attendance: 5,000 (19th November 1955)
Pitch Size: 110 × 70 yards

Colours: Shirts are Blue with White trim, White shorts
Telephone Nº: (0121) 661-9392
Fax Number: (0121) 314-5321
Ground Capacity: 3,150
Seating Capacity: 525
Web site: www.halesowentownfc.co.uk

GENERAL INFORMATION

Car Parking: 20 spaces available at the Social Club.
Coach Parking: Available near to the ground
Nearest Railway Station: Old Hill (2 miles)
Nearest Bus Station: Halesowen Town Centre
Club Shop: At the ground
Opening Times: Matchdays only
Telephone Nº: –

GROUND INFORMATION

Away Supporters' Entrances & Sections:
No usual segregation

ADMISSION INFO (2010/2011 PRICES)

Adult Standing/Seating: £10.00
Concessionary Standing/Seating: £7.00
Child Standing/Seating: £2.00 (When accompanied by a paying adult)
Programme Price: £1.50

DISABLED INFORMATION

Wheelchairs: 5 spaces available in total situated at the side of the Main Seating Stand
Helpers: Admitted
Prices: Free of charge for the disabled
Disabled Toilets: Available near the Main Stand
Contact: (0121) 661-9392   (Bookings are not necessary)

Travelling Supporters' Information:
Routes: Exit the M5 at Junction 3 and follow the A456 towards Kidderminster. At the first roundabout, turn right onto the A458 towards Dudley. Turn left at the next roundabout and follow signposts onto the A458 towards Stourbridge. Take the 3rd exit at the next roundabout and the ground is on the left hand side after approximately 400 yards.

HEDNESFORD TOWN FC

Founded: 1880
Former Names: Formed by the amalgamation of West Hill FC and Hill Top FC
Nickname: 'The Pitmen'
Ground: Keys Park, Keys Park Road, Hednesford, Cannock   WS12 2DZ
Record Attendance: 3,169 (13th January 1997)

Colours: White shirts with Black shorts
Telephone N°: (01543) 422870
Fax Number: (01543) 428180
Ground Capacity: 6,039
Seating Capacity: 1,011
Web site: www.hednesfordfc.co.uk

GENERAL INFORMATION
Car Parking: 500 spaces available at the ground – £1.00 fee
Coach Parking: At the ground
Nearest Railway Station: Hednesford (1 mile)
Nearest Bus Station: Hednesford
Club Shop: At the ground
Opening Times: Matchdays and Weekdays 9.00am–5.00pm
Telephone N°: (01543) 422870

GROUND INFORMATION
Away Supporters' Entrances & Sections:
No usual segregation

ADMISSION INFO (2010/2011 PRICES)
Adult Standing: £8.00
Adult Seating: £10.00
Concessionary Standing: £5.00
Concessionary Seating: £6.00
Programme Price: £2.00

DISABLED INFORMATION
Wheelchairs: 8 spaces available in front of the Main Stand
Helpers: Please contact the club for details
Prices: Please contact the club for details
Disabled Toilets: 2 are available – one in the Main Building, one in the Hednesford End of the stand
Contact: (01543) 422870   (Bookings are necessary)

Travelling Supporters' Information:
Routes: Exit the M6 at Junction 11 or the M6 Toll T7 and follow signs for A460 (Rugeley). After crossing the A5 at Churchbridge Island, continue on the A460. After five traffic islands pick up signs for Hednesford Town FC/Keys Park and follow to the ground.

HEMEL HEMPSTEAD TOWN FC

Founded: 1885
Former Names: Apsley FC and Hemel Hempstead FC
Nickname: 'The Tudors'
Ground: Vauxhall Road, Adeyfield, Hemel Hempstead HP2 4HW
Record Attendance: 2,000 (vs Watford – 1985)
Pitch Size: 112 × 72 yards

Colours: Shirts and Shorts are Red with White trim
Telephone Nº: (01442) 259777
Fax Number: (01442) 264322
Ground Capacity: 2,500
Seating Capacity: 350
Web site: www.hemelfc.com

GENERAL INFORMATION
Car Parking: At the ground
Coach Parking: At the ground
Nearest Railway Station: Hemel Hempstead (1½ miles)
Nearest Bus Station: Hemel Hempstead (¾ mile)
Club Shop: None

GROUND INFORMATION
Away Supporters' Entrances & Sections:
No usual segregation

ADMISSION INFO (2010/2011 PRICES)
Adult Standing: £8.00
Adult Seating: £8.00
Concessionary Standing/Seating: £5.00
Junior Standing/Seating: £1.00
Programme Price: £1.00

DISABLED INFORMATION
Wheelchairs: Accommodated
Helpers: Admitted
Prices: Normal prices apply
Disabled Toilets: Available in the Clubhouse
Contact: (01442) 259777

Travelling Supporters' Information:
Routes: Exit the M1 at Junction 8 and go straight ahead at the first roundabout. When approaching the 2nd roundabout move into the right hand lane and, as you continue straight across be ready to turn right almost immediately through a gap in the central reservation. This turn-off is Leverstock Green Road and continue along this to the double mini-roundabout. At this roundabout turn left into Vauxhall Road and the ground is on the right at the next roundabout.

LEAMINGTON FC

Founded: 1891
Former Names: Leamington Town FC, Lockheed Borg & Beck FC, AP Leamington FC and Lockheed Leamington FC
Nickname: 'The Brakes'
Ground: New Windmill Ground, Harbury Lane, Whitnash, Leamington   CV33 9JR

Record Attendance: 1,380 (17th February 2007)
Colours: Gold and Black shirts with Black shorts
Telephone Nº: (01926) 430406
Fax Number: (01926) 430406
Ground Capacity: 5,000
Seating Capacity: 120
Web Site: www.leamingtonfc.co.uk

GENERAL INFORMATION
Car Parking: At the ground
Coach Parking: At the ground
Nearest Railway Station: Leamington (4 miles)
Club Shop: At the ground
Opening Times: Matchdays only
Telephone Nº: –

GROUND INFORMATION
Away Supporters' Entrances & Sections:
No usual segregation

ADMISSION INFO (2010/2011 PRICES)
Adult Standing: £8.00   **Adult Seating:** £8.00
Senior Citizen/Junior Standing: £5.00
Senior Citizen/Junior Seating: £5.00
Programme Price: £1.50

DISABLED INFORMATION
Wheelchairs: Accommodated
Helpers: Admitted
Prices: Normal prices apply for the disabled. Helpers are admitted free of charge
Disabled Toilets: Available
Contact: (01926) 430406   (Bookings are not necessary)

Travelling Supporters' Information:
Routes: Exit the M40 at Junction 14 and take the A452 towards Leamington continuing at the roundabout into Europa Way (still A452). After approximately ½ mile, take the 4th exit at the roundabout into Harbury Lane (signposted for Harbury and Bishops Tachbrook). Continue on Harbury lane, taking the 3rd exit at the first roundabout and going straight ahead at the traffic lights. The ground is on the left hand side of the road after approximately 1½ miles.

OXFORD CITY FC

Founded: 1882
Former Names: None
Nickname: 'City'
Ground: Court Place Farm, Marsh Lane, Marston, Oxford   OX3 0NQ
Record Attendance: 9,500 (1950)

Colours: Blue & White hooped shirts with Blue shorts
Telephone N°: (01865) 744493
Ground Capacity: 3,000
Seating Capacity: 300
Web Site: www.oxfordcityfc.co.uk

GENERAL INFORMATION
Car Parking: At the ground
Coach Parking: At the ground
Nearest Railway Station: Oxford (3¾ miles)
Club Shop: At the ground
Opening Times: Matchdays only
Telephone N°: (01865) 744493

GROUND INFORMATION
Away Supporters' Entrances & Sections:
No usual segregation

ADMISSION INFO (2010/2011 PRICES)
Adult Standing/Seating: £9.00
Concessionary Standing/Seating: £4.50
Under-16s Standing/Seating: Free of charge
Programme Price: £1.50

DISABLED INFORMATION
Wheelchairs: Accommodated
Helpers: Admitted
Prices: Normal prices apply for the disabled and helpers
Disabled Toilets: Available
Contact: (01865) 744493   (Bookings are not necessary)

Travelling Supporters' Information:
Routes: The stadium is located by the side of the A40 Northern Bypass Road next to the Marston flyover junction to the north east of Oxford. Exit the A40 at the Marston junction and head into Marsh Lane (B4150). Take the first turn on the left into the OXSRAD Complex then turn immediately left again to follow the approach road to the stadium in the far corner of the site.

SALISBURY CITY FC

Founded: 1947
Former Names: Salisbury FC
Nickname: 'The Whites'
Ground: The Raymond McEnhill Stadium, Partridge Way, Old Sarum, Salisbury, Wiltshire SP4 6PU
Record Attendance: 2,633 (19th January 2008)
Pitch Size: 115 × 76 yards

Colours: White shirts with Black shorts
Telephone Nº: (01722) 776655
Fax Number: (01722) 323100
Ground Capacity: 5,000
Seating Capacity: 500
Web site: www.salisburycity-fc.co.uk

GENERAL INFORMATION
Car Parking: At the ground
Coach Parking: At the ground
Nearest Railway Station: Salisbury (2½ miles)
Nearest Bus Station: Salisbury
Club Shop: At the ground + an online shop
Opening Times: Office Hours and Matchdays
Telephone Nº: (01722) 776655
Postal Sales: Yes

GROUND INFORMATION
Away Supporters' Entrances & Sections:
No usual segregation

ADMISSION INFO (2010/2011 PRICES)
Adult Standing: £9.00
Adult Seating: £10.00
Senior Citizen Standing: £7.00
Senior Citizen Seating: £8.00
Under-16s Standing: £3.00   (Students: £7.00)
Under-16s Seating: £5.00   (Students: £9.00)
Programme Price: £2.50

DISABLED INFORMATION
Wheelchairs: Accommodated in a special area in the Main Stand. A stairlift is available.
Helpers: Admitted free of charge
Prices: Normal prices apply for the disabled
Disabled Toilets: Available
Contact: (01722) 776655   (Bookings are necessary)

Travelling Supporters' Information:
Routes: The Stadium well signposted and is situated off the main A345 Salisbury to Amesbury road on the northern edge of the City, 2 miles from the City Centre.

STOURBRIDGE FC

Founded: 1876
Former Names: Stourbridge Standard FC
Nickname: 'The Glassboys'
Ground: War Memorial Ground, High Street, Amblecote, Stourbridge   DY8 4HN
Record Attendance: 5,726 (1974)

Colours: Red and White striped shirts with Red shorts
Telephone N°: (01384) 394040
Ground Capacity: 2,000
Seating Capacity: 250
Web Site: www.stourbridgefc.com
E-mail: admin@stourbridgefc.com

GENERAL INFORMATION

Car Parking: At the ground
Coach Parking: Please contact the club for information
Nearest Railway Station: Stourbridge Town (¾ mile)
Club Shop: At the ground
Opening Times: Matchdays only from 1 hour before kick-off
Telephone N°: (01384) 394040

GROUND INFORMATION

Away Supporters' Entrances & Sections:
No usual segregation

ADMISSION INFO (2010/2011 PRICES)

Adult Standing/Seating: £8.00
Senior Citizen Standing/Seating: £4.00
Under-16s Standing/Seating: £4.00
Note: Under-11s are admitted free of charge when accompanied by a paying adult
Programme Price: £1.50

DISABLED INFORMATION

Wheelchairs: Accommodated
Helpers: Admitted
Prices: Normal prices apply for the disabled and helpers
Disabled Toilets:
Contact: (01384) 394040   (Bookings are necessary)

Travelling Supporters' Information:
Routes: From the South: Exit the M5 at Junction 4 and take the A491 to Stourbridge. Continue along the A491, pass Hagley then go through Pedmore and Old Swinford before joining the Stourbridge Ring Road (one-way). Follow the lane signs for Wolverhampton A491. Pass through three sets of traffic lights before reaching the ground which is on the left hand side of the road, opposite the Royal Oak Public House; From the North or East: Exit the M5 at Junction 3 and take the A456 towards Stourbridge and Kidderminster. After about five miles, turn right at the traffic lights in Hagley to join the A491 and follow into Stourbridge passing through Pedmore and Old Swinford onto the Stourbridge Ring-Road (one-way) as above.

SWINDON SUPERMARINE FC

Founded: 1992
Former Names: None
Nickname: 'Marine'
Ground: Hunts Copse, Supermarine Road, Swindon, SN3 4SZ
Record Attendance: 1,550

Colours: Blue and White shirts with Blue shorts
Telephone Nº: (01793) 828778
Fax Number: (01793) 790865
Ground Capacity: 3,000
Seating Capacity: 345
Web Site: www.swindonsupermarinefc.com

GENERAL INFORMATION

Car Parking: 200 spaces at the ground (£1.00 charge per car)
Coach Parking: At the ground
Nearest Railway Station: Swindon (4 miles)
Club Shop: At the ground
Opening Times: Matchdays only
Telephone Nº: (01793) 828778

GROUND INFORMATION

Away Supporters' Entrances & Sections:
No usual segregation

ADMISSION INFO (2010/2011 PRICES)

Adult Standing: £9.00   **Adult Seating:** £9.00
Senior Citizen/Under-16s Standing: £5.00
Senior Citizen/Under-16s Seating: £5.00
Note: Under-11s are admitted free of charge when accompanied by a paying adult
Programme Price: £1.50

DISABLED INFORMATION

Wheelchairs: Accommodated
Helpers: Admitted
Prices: Normal prices apply for the disabled and helpers
Disabled Toilets: Available
Contact: (01793) 828778   (Bookings are not necessary)

Travelling Supporters' Information:
Routes: The ground is located next to the South Marston Industrial Estate just off the A361 to the north of Swindon and south of Highworth. Follow the signs for the Industrial Estate then turn into Supermarine Road at the roundabout to the north of the industrial estate. The ground is on the left hand side of the road, opposite the industrial estate.

TIVERTON TOWN FC

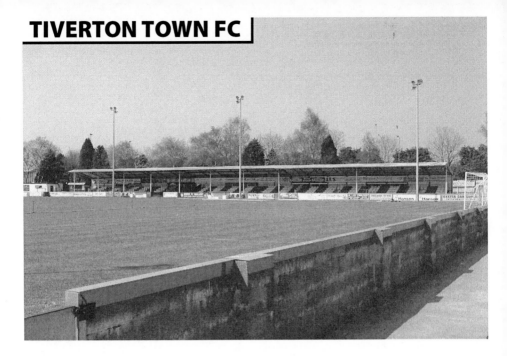

Founded: 1920
Former Names: None
Nickname: 'Tivvy'
Ground: Ladysmead, Bolham Road, Tiverton, EX16 6SG
Record Attendance: 3,000 (1994)

Colours: Yellow shirts and shorts
Telephone Nº: (01884) 252397
Ground Capacity: 3,000
Seating Capacity: 520
Web site: www.tivertontownfc.com

GENERAL INFORMATION

Car Parking: At the ground
Coach Parking: At the ground
Nearest Railway Station: Tiverton Parkway (7 miles)
Nearest Bus Station: Tiverton
Club Shop: At the ground
Opening Times: Matchdays only
Telephone Nº: (01884) 252397

GROUND INFORMATION

Away Supporters' Entrances & Sections:
No usual segregation

ADMISSION INFO (2010/2011 PRICES)

Adult Standing: £8.00
Adult Seating: £9.00
Under-16s Standing: £1.00
Under-16s Seating: £2.00
Senior Citizen Standing: £5.50
Senior Citizen Seating: £6.50
Programme Price: £2.00

DISABLED INFORMATION

Wheelchairs: Accommodated
Helpers: Admitted
Prices: Normal prices apply
Disabled Toilets: Available
Contact: (01884) 252397 (Bookings are not necessary)

Travelling Supporters' Information:
Routes: Exit the M5 at Junction 27 and follow the A361 towards Tiverton for about 7 miles. Ignore the first junction for the A396 (Tiverton and Bickleigh) at Gornhay Cross and keep going until you reach a large roundabout. Turn left at the roundabout (A3126) for the Town Centre and Castle and continue along for about 400 yards. Cross the new roundabout passing the College Sports Field and Rugby Club and the ground is then on the right just by R & M Cars.

TRURO CITY FC

Unfortunately, no ground photograph
for Truro City FC was available
at the time of going to press.

Founded: 1889
Former Names: None
Nickname: 'White Tigers' or 'Tinmen'
Ground: Treyew Road, Truro   TR1 2TH
Record Attendance: 2,000 (3rd October 2006)

Colours: All White shirts and shorts
Telephone N°: (01872) 225400
Fax Number: (01872) 225402
Ground Capacity: 3,000
Seating Capacity: 500
Web Site: www.trurocityfc.co.uk

GENERAL INFORMATION
Car Parking: At the ground
Coach Parking: At the ground
Nearest Railway Station: Truro (½ mile)
Club Shop: None
Opening Times: –
Telephone N°: –

GROUND INFORMATION
Away Supporters' Entrances & Sections:
No usual segregation

ADMISSION INFO (2010/2011 PRICES)
Adult Standing: £10.00
Adult Seating: £10.00
Senior Citizen Standing: £7.00
Senior Citizen Seating: £7.00
Under-16s Standing/Seating: Free of charge
Programme Price: £2.00

DISABLED INFORMATION
Wheelchairs: Accommodated
Helpers: Admitted
Prices: Normal prices apply for the disabled and helpers
Disabled Toilets: None
Contact: (01872) 225400   (Bookings are not necessary)

Travelling Supporters' Information:
Routes: From the North or East: Take the A30 to the A390 (from the North) or travel straight on the A390 (from the East) to Truro. Continue on the A390 and pass through Truro. The ground is located just to the South West of Truro on the left hand side of the A390 just before the County Hall; From the West: Take the A390 to Truro. The ground is on the right hand side of the road shortly after crossing the railway line and passing the County Hall; From the South: Take the A39 to Truro. At the junction with the A390 turn left onto Green Lane and the ground is on the left hand side of the road after approximately ½ mile.

WEYMOUTH FC

Founded: 1890
Former Names: None
Nickname: 'Terras'
Ground: Wessex Stadium, Radipole Lane, Weymouth, Dorset   DT4 9XJ
Record Attendance: 6,500 (14th November 2005)

Colours: Shirts are Claret and Sky Blue, Claret shorts
Telephone Nº: 08721 840000
Fax Number: (0117) 327-0298
Ground Capacity: 6,500
Seating Capacity: 800
Web site: www.theterras.co.uk

GENERAL INFORMATION
Car Parking: 200 spaces available at the ground
Coach Parking: At the ground
Nearest Railway Station: Weymouth (2 miles)
Nearest Bus Station: Weymouth Town Centre
Club Shop: At the ground
Opening Times: Matchdays only
Telephone Nº: –

GROUND INFORMATION
Away Supporters' Entrances & Sections:
No usual segregation

ADMISSION INFO (2010/2011 PRICES)
Adult Standing: £9.50
Adult Seating: £9.50
Senior Citizen/Student Standing: £6.00
Senior Citizen/Student Seating: £6.00
Under-16s Standing: £2.50
Under-16s Seating: £2.50
Programme Price: –

DISABLED INFORMATION
Wheelchairs: Accommodated
Helpers: Admitted
Prices: Normal prices apply for the disabled. Free for helpers
Disabled Toilets: Yes
Contact: (01305) 785558   (Bookings are not necessary)

Travelling Supporters' Information:
Routes: Take the A354 from Dorchester to Weymouth and turn right at the first roundabout to the town centre. Take the 3rd exit at the next roundabout and follow signs for the ground which is about ½ mile on the right.

WINDSOR & ETON FC

Founded: 1892
Former Names: None
Nickname: 'The Royalists'
Ground: Stag Meadow, St.Leonards Road, Windsor, SL4 3DR
Record Attendance: 8,000
Pitch Size: 110 × 78 yards

Colours: Shirts and shorts are Red with Green trim
Telephone Nº: (01753) 860656
Fax Number: (01753) 860656
Ground Capacity: 4,500
Seating Capacity: 400
Web site: www.wefc.co.uk

GENERAL INFORMATION
Car Parking: At the ground
Coach Parking: At the ground
Nearest Railway Station: Windsor & Eton Central
Nearest Bus Station: Slough
Club Shop: At the ground
Opening Times: Matchdays only
Telephone Nº: (01753) 860656

GROUND INFORMATION
Away Supporters' Entrances & Sections:
No usual segregation

ADMISSION INFO (2010/2011 PRICES)
Adult Standing: £9.00   **Adult Seating**: £9.00
Senior Citizen Standing: £5.00
Senior Citizen Seating: £5.00
Note: Under-16s are admitted free of charge when accompanied by a paying adult
Programme Price: £2.00

DISABLED INFORMATION
Wheelchairs: Accommodated
Helpers: Admitted
Prices: Normal prices apply
Disabled Toilets: None
Contact: (01753) 860656

Travelling Supporters' Information:
Routes: Exit the M4 at Junction 6 and take the A355 to the roundabout. At the roundabout, take the 3rd exit (signposted for Ascot & Bracknell) and continue to the T-junction. Turn left at the T-junction into St. Leonards Road and the ground is ¼ mile on the right opposite the Stag & Hounds Public House.

28

THE ZAMARETTO LEAGUE DIVISION ONE CENTRAL

Secretary Jason Mills

Correspondence
secretary@southern-football-league.co.uk

Web Site www.southern-football-league.co.uk

Clubs for the 2010/2011 Season

AFC HAYES

Founded: 1974
Former Names: Brook House FC
Nickname: 'The Brook'
Ground: Farm Park, Kingshill Avenue, Hayes, UB4 8DD
Record Attendance: 1,800 (vs Chelsea in the Middlesex Cup)

Colours: Blue and White striped shirts with Blue shorts
Telephone N°: (020) 8845-0110
Fax Number: (020) 8842-1448
Ground Capacity: 2,000
Seating Capacity: 150
Web Site: www.pitchero.com/clubs/afchayes

GENERAL INFORMATION

Car Parking: At the ground
Coach Parking: At the ground
Nearest Railway Station: South Ruislip (1¾ miles)
Nearest Tube Station: South Ruislip (3 miles)
Club Shop: None
Opening Times: –
Telephone N°: –

GROUND INFORMATION

Away Supporters' Entrances & Sections:
No usual segregation

ADMISSION INFO (2010/2011 PRICES)

Adult Standing: £8.00
Adult Seating: £8.00
Senior Citizen/Junior Standing: £5.00
Senior Citizen/Junior Seating: £5.00
Programme Price: £1.50

DISABLED INFORMATION

Wheelchairs: Accommodated
Helpers: Admitted
Prices: Normal prices apply for the disabled and helpers
Disabled Toilets: None
Contact: (020) 8845-0110 (Bookings are not necessary)

Travelling Supporters' Information:
Routes: Take the A40 (Western Avenue) to the McDonalds Target roundabout then join the A312 heading south towards Hayes. At the White Hart roundabout, take the 3rd exit into Yeading Lane then turn right at the first set of traffic lights into Kingshill Avenue. The ground is on the right after about a mile.

ARLESEY TOWN FC

Founded: 1891
Former Names: None
Nickname: 'The Blues'
Ground: Armadillo Stadium, Hitchin Road, Arlesey, SG15 6RS
Record Attendance: 2,000 (1906)

Colours: Light and Dark Blue quartered shirts with Dark Blue shorts
Telephone Nº: (01462) 734504
Ground Capacity: 2,920
Seating Capacity: 150
Web Site: www.arleseyfc.co.uk

GENERAL INFORMATION
Car Parking: At the ground
Coach Parking: At the ground
Nearest Railway Station: Arlesey (1¾ miles)
Club Shop: In the Clubhouse at the ground
Opening Times: Matchdays only
Telephone Nº: –

GROUND INFORMATION
Away Supporters' Entrances & Sections:
No usual segregation

ADMISSION INFO (2010/2011 PRICES)
Adult Standing: £5.00
Adult Seating: £5.00
Senior Citizen/Junior Standing: £2.00
Senior Citizen/Junior Seating: £2.00
Programme Price: –

DISABLED INFORMATION
Wheelchairs: Accommodated
Helpers: Admitted
Prices: Normal prices apply for the disabled and helpers
Disabled Toilets: Available in the Clubhouse
Contact: (01462) 734504 (Bookings are necessary)

Travelling Supporters' Information:
Routes: Exit the A1(M) at Junction 10 and take the A507 towards Stotford and Shefford. At the 3rd roundabout, take the first exit along Stotfold Road. Take the first turn on the left into House Lane which becomes the High Street and continue for approximately 1 mile. The ground is clearly visible on the left hand side of the road opposite the Hampden Business Centre.

ASHFORD TOWN (MIDDLESEX) FC

Founded: 1964
Former Names: Formed by the amalgamation of Ashford Albion FC and Staines Youth Club
Nickname: 'Tangerines'
Ground: Short Lane Stadium, Short Lane, Stanwell, Staines TW19 7BH
Record Attendance: 750 vs Brentford (1986)
Pitch Size: 111 × 73 yards

Colours: Tangerine and White striped shirts with Black shorts
Telephone N°: (01784) 245908
Fax Number: (01784) 253913
Ground Capacity: 2,550
Seating Capacity: 250
Web site: www.ashfordtownmiddlesexfc.com

GENERAL INFORMATION
Car Parking: At the ground
Coach Parking: At the ground
Nearest Railway Station: Ashford (Middlesex) (1 mile)
Nearest Tube Station: Hatton Cross (3 miles)
Club Shop: In the Clubhouse
Opening Times: Matchdays only
Telephone N°: (01784) 245908

GROUND INFORMATION
Away Supporters' Entrances & Sections:
No usual segregation

ADMISSION INFO (2010/2011 PRICES)
Adult Standing/Seating: £8.00
Concessionary Standing/Seating: £5.00
Under-16s Standing/Seating: £2.00
Programme Price: £1.00

DISABLED INFORMATION
Wheelchairs: Accommodated
Helpers: Admitted
Prices: Free of charge for the disabled
Disabled Toilets: Available
Contact: (01784) 245908 (Bookings are not necessary)

Travelling Supporters' Information:
Routes: Exit the M25 at Junction 13 and follow the A30 towards London. After passing Ashford Hospital on the left, take the 3rd turning on the left into Short Lane (adjacent to the footbridge) and the ground is on the right hand side after ¼ mile.

ATHERSTONE TOWN FC

Founded: 1887 (Re-formed 2004)
Former Names: Atherstone United FC
Nickname: 'The Adders'
Ground: Sheepy Road, Atherstone   CV9 1HG
Record Attendance: 2,979 (vs Rugby Town)
Pitch Size: 115 × 80 yards

Colours: Red and White striped shirts with Red shorts
Telephone N°: (01827) 717829 (Matchdays only)
Ground Capacity: 3,500
Seating Capacity: 353
Web site: www.atherstonetownfc.co.uk

GENERAL INFORMATION
Car Parking: Adjacent to the ground
Coach Parking: Adjacent to the ground
Nearest Railway Station: Atherstone (1 mile)
Nearest Bus Station: Atherstone or Nuneaton
Club Shop: At the ground
Opening Times: Matchdays only
Telephone N°: (01827) 717829

GROUND INFORMATION
Away Supporters' Entrances & Sections:
Gipsy Lane entrances and accommodation

ADMISSION INFO (2010/2011 PRICES)
Adult Standing: £7.00
Adult Seating: £7.00
Concessionary Standing: £3.00
Concessionary Seating: £3.00
Note: Under-14s are admitted free of charge when
accompanied by a paying adult
Programme Price: £1.50

DISABLED INFORMATION
Wheelchairs: 4 spaces available in the Centre Stand
Helpers: Please phone the club for information
Prices: Please phone the club for information
Disabled Toilets: None
Contact: (01827) 717829   (Bookings are not necessary)

Travelling Supporters' Information:
Routes: Take the A5 into Atherstone then follow signs for Twycross and Sheepy Magna. The ground is on the left after ½ mile.

AYLESBURY FC

Unfortunately, no ground photograph
for Aylesbury FC was available
at the time of going to press.

Founded: 1930 (As Stocklake FC)
Former Names: Stocklake FC, Belgrave FC, Haywood United FC and Aylesbury Vale FC
Nickname: 'The Moles'
Ground: Haywood Way, Aylesbury   HP19 9WZ
Record Attendance: 250

Colours: Red and Black shirts with Black shorts
Telephone Nº: (01296) 421101
Fax Number: (01296) 421101
Ground Capacity: 1,000
Seating Capacity: 50
Web Site: www.aylesburyfootballclub.co.uk

GENERAL INFORMATION
Car Parking: Limited number of spaces at the ground
Coach Parking: At the ground
Nearest Railway Station: Aylesbury (2 miles)
Club Shop: Via the Club's web site only
Opening Times: –
Telephone Nº: –

GROUND INFORMATION
Away Supporters' Entrances & Sections:
No usual segregation

ADMISSION INFO (2010/2011 PRICES)
Adult Standing: £7.00
Adult Seating: £7.00
Senior Citizen Standing: £5.50
Senior Citizen Seating: £5.50
Under-16s Standing: £1.50
Under-16s Seating: £1.50
Programme Price: £1.00

DISABLED INFORMATION
Wheelchairs: Accommodated
Helpers: Admitted
Prices: Normal prices apply for the disabled and helpers
Disabled Toilets: Available
Contact: (01296) 421101   (Bookings are not necessary)

Travelling Supporters' Information:
Routes: Take the A41 (Bicester Road) to the north-western outskirts of Aylesbury near to Rabans Lane Industrial Estate. Turn into Jackson Road at the roundabout at the edge of town and Haywood Way is the 2nd turning on the left. The ground is at the end of the lane.

BARTON ROVERS FC

Founded: 1898
Former Names: None
Nickname: 'Rovers'
Ground: Sharpenhoe Road, Barton-le-Clay, MK45 4SD
Record Attendance: 1,900 (1976)

Colours: Yellow shirts with Black shorts
Telephone Nº: (01582) 707772
Fax Number: (01582) 707772
Ground Capacity: 4,000
Seating Capacity: 160
Web Site: www.bartonrovers.co.uk

GENERAL INFORMATION

Car Parking: At the ground
Coach Parking: At the ground
Nearest Railway Station: Harlington (3½ miles)
Club Shop: None
Opening Times: –
Telephone Nº: –

GROUND INFORMATION

Away Supporters' Entrances & Sections:
No usual segregation

ADMISSION INFO (2010/2011 PRICES)

Adult Standing: £8.00
Adult Seating: £8.00
Senior Citizen/Junior Standing: £5.00
Senior Citizen/Junior Seating: £5.00
Programme Price: £1.50

DISABLED INFORMATION

Wheelchairs: Accommodated
Helpers: Admitted
Prices: Normal prices apply for the disabled and helpers
Disabled Toilets: Available
Contact: (01582) 707772   (Bookings are necessary)

Travelling Supporters' Information:
Routes: The ground is located in Barton-le-Clay which is about 5 miles to the north of Luton by the side of the A6 road. Take the A6 to Barton-le-Clay and exit at the roundabout onto the B655 into Barton itself. Continue along the B655 Bedford Road then turn right at the mini-roundabout into Sharpenhoe Road. The entrance to the ground is on the left just after the houses.

BEACONSFIELD SYCOB FC

Founded: 1994
Former Names: Formed by the amalgamation of Beaconsfield United FC and Slough YCOB FC
Nickname: 'The Rams'
Ground: Holloways Park, Slough Road, Beaconsfield   HP9 2SE
Record Attendance: 3,000 (1985)

Colours: Red & White quartered shirts, Black shorts
Telephone N°: (01494) 676868
Fax Number: (01753) 865081
Ground Capacity: 3,000
Seating Capacity: 250
Web site: www.pitchero.com/clubs/beaconsfieldsycob

GENERAL INFORMATION
Car Parking: At the ground
Coach Parking: At the ground
Nearest Railway Station: Beaconsfield (2½ miles)
Club Shop: At the ground
Opening Times: Matchdays only
Telephone N°: (01494) 676868

GROUND INFORMATION
Away Supporters' Entrances & Sections:
No usual segregation

ADMISSION INFO (2010/2011 PRICES)
Adult Standing: £7.50
Adult Seating: £7.50
Senior Citizen/Junior Standing: £4.00
Senior Citizen/Junior Seating: £4.00
Programme Price: £2.00

DISABLED INFORMATION
Wheelchairs: Accommodated
Helpers: Admitted
Prices: Normal prices apply for the disabled and helpers
Disabled Toilets: Available
Contact: (01494) 676868   (Bookings are necessary)

Travelling Supporters' Information:
Routes: Exit the M40 at Junction 2 and head into the Beaconsfield Motorway Service area. In the services, follow the signs for Beaconsfield SYCOB, crossing the A355 and heading back towards the M40. After approximately 150 yards turn left into the ground and the car park and Clubhouse are on the right after 200 yards.

BEDFONT TOWN FC

Founded: 1965
Former Names: Bedfont Green FC
Nickname: 'The Peacocks'
Ground: The Orchard, Hatton Road, Bedfont, TW14 9QT
Record Attendance: 259 (18th August 2010)

Colours: Navy Blue shirts and shorts
Telephone Nº: (020) 8890-7264
Ground Capacity: 1,200
Seating Capacity: 150
Web Site: www.bedfonttownfc.co.uk

GENERAL INFORMATION

Car Parking: At the ground
Coach Parking: At the ground
Nearest Railway Station: Heathrow Terminal 4 (1 mile)
Nearest Tube Station: Hatton Cross (½ mile)
Club Shop: None at present
Opening Times: –
Telephone Nº: –

GROUND INFORMATION

Away Supporters' Entrances & Sections:
Segregation is only in place on rare occasions – please contact the club for further details

ADMISSION INFO (2010/2011 PRICES)

Adult Standing: £8.00
Adult Seating: £8.00
Senior Citizen/Junior Standing: £4.00
Senior Citizen/Junior Seating: £4.00
Programme Price: £1.50

DISABLED INFORMATION

Wheelchairs: Accommodated
Helpers: Admitted
Prices: Concessionary prices are charged for the disabled and helpers
Disabled Toilets: Available
Contact: (020) 8890-7264 (Bookings are not necessary)

Travelling Supporters' Information:
Routes: The ground is located just next to Heathrow Airport southern perimeter. Take the A30 Great South-West Road and turn south into Hatton Road at the junction next to Hatton Cross Tube station. Turn immediately right to continue along Hatton Road and the ground is on the left hand side of the road after approximately ½ mile.

BEDWORTH UNITED FC

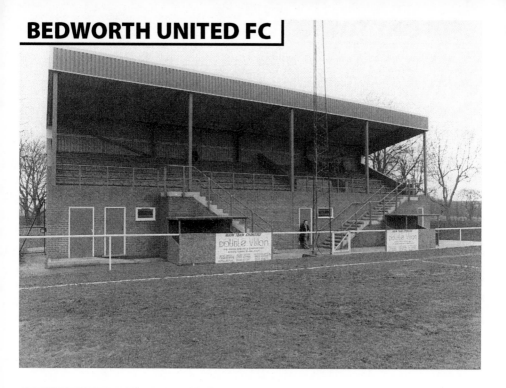

Founded: 1895
Former Names: Bedworth Town FC
Nickname: 'The Greenbacks'
Ground: The Oval, Miners Welfare Park,
Coventry Road, Bedworth   CV12 8NN
Record Attendance: 5,127 (23rd February 1982)

Colours: Yellow shirts and shorts
Telephone Nº: (02476) 314752
Ground Capacity: 7,000
Seating Capacity: 300
Web Site: www.bedworthunited.co.uk

GENERAL INFORMATION

Car Parking: Limited number of spaces available at the ground and Town Centre car parks are a short walk
Coach Parking: At the ground
Nearest Railway Station: Bedworth (¼ mile)
Club Shop: At the ground
Opening Times: Matchdays only
Telephone Nº: (02476) 314752

GROUND INFORMATION

Away Supporters' Entrances & Sections:
No usual segregation

ADMISSION INFO (2010/2011 PRICES)

Adult Standing: £7.00
Adult Seating: £7.00
Senior Citizen/Junior Standing: £5.00
Senior Citizen/Junior Seating: £5.00
Programme Price: £1.50

DISABLED INFORMATION

Wheelchairs: Accommodated
Helpers: Admitted
Prices: Normal prices apply for the disabled and helpers
Disabled Toilets: Available
Contact: (02476) 314752   (Bookings are not necessary)

Travelling Supporters' Information:
Routes: Exit the M6 at Junction 3 and follow signs for the B4113. At the next roundabout, take the first exit and head north, passing underneath the M6 and continuing up Longford Road into Coventry Road. The entrance to the ground is on the right after passing the cemetery on the left. Take the 3rd exit at the mini-roundabout.

BIGGLESWADE TOWN FC

Founded: 1874
Former Names: Biggleswade FC
Nickname: 'The Waders'
Ground: The Carlsberg Stadium, Langford Road, Biggleswade   SG18 9JT
Record Attendance: Approximately 2,000

Colours: Green & White striped shirts, Green shorts
Telephone N°: (01767) 315547
Fax Number: (01767) 315547
Ground Capacity: 3,000
Seating Capacity: 300
Web Site: www.biggleswadetownfc.co.uk

GENERAL INFORMATION
Car Parking: At the ground
Coach Parking: At the ground
Nearest Railway Station: Biggleswade (½ mile)
Club Shop: At the ground
Opening Times: Matchdays only
Telephone N°: –

GROUND INFORMATION
Away Supporters' Entrances & Sections:
No usual segregation

ADMISSION INFO (2010/2011 PRICES)
Adult Standing: £8.00
Adult Seating: £8.00
Concessionary Standing: £5.00
Concessionary Seating: £5.00
Note: Under-13s are admitted free of charge when accompanied by a paying adult
Programme Price: Included in admission prices

DISABLED INFORMATION
Wheelchairs: Accommodated
Helpers: Admitted
Prices: Normal prices apply for the disabled and helpers
Disabled Toilets: Available
Contact: (01767) 315547   (Bookings are not necessary)

Travelling Supporters' Information:
Routes: The Stadium is located just to the South of the A1 at Biggleswade. Exit the A1 at the northernmost roundabout by the Sainsbury's superstore and follow the A6001 (Hill Lane) into Biggleswade. Continue heading southwards along the A6001 into Shortmead Street then turn right at the mini-roundabout into St. Andrews Street. Continue along then turn right at the traffic lights shortly after the bend in the road onto Hitchin Street. Go straight on at the next two roundabouts, pass under the A1 and the entrance to the ground is on the right, after approximately 200 yards.

BURNHAM FC

Founded: 1878
Former Names: None
Nickname: 'The Blues'
Ground: The Gore, Wymers Wood Road, Burnham, Slough SL1 8JG
Record Attendance: 2,380 (2nd April 1983)

Colours: Blue & White quartered shirts with Blue shorts
Telephone N°: 07771 677337
Fax Number: (01628) 668654
Ground Capacity: 2,500
Seating Capacity: 300
Web Site: www.burnhamfc.com

GENERAL INFORMATION
Car Parking: At the ground
Coach Parking: At the ground
Nearest Railway Station: Taplow (1½ miles)
Club Shop: None
Opening Times: –
Telephone N°: –

GROUND INFORMATION
Away Supporters' Entrances & Sections:
No usual segregation

ADMISSION INFO (2010/2011 PRICES)
Adult Standing: £8.00
Adult Seating: £8.00
Concessionary Standing: £4.00
Concessionary Seating: £4.00
Junior Standing: £1.00
Junior Seating: £1.00
Programme Price: £1.50

DISABLED INFORMATION
Wheelchairs: Accommodated
Helpers: Admitted
Prices: Normal prices apply for the disabled and helpers
Disabled Toilets: Available
Contact: 07771 677337 (Bookings are not necessary)

Travelling Supporters' Information:
Routes: Exit the M4 at Junction 7 and turn left onto the A4 signposted for Maidenhead. After a short distance, turn right at the roundabout by Sainsbury's into Lent Rise Road and continue, passing under the railway line and going straight on at two roundabouts before forking right into Wymers Wood Road. The ground is on the right hand side of the road almost immediately.

DAVENTRY TOWN FC

Founded: 1886
Former Names: None
Nickname: 'Town'
Ground: Communications Park, Browns Road, Daventry NN11 4NS
Record Attendance: 850 (1989)

Colours: Violet shirts and shorts
Telephone Nº: 0844 846-8228 (Office)
Fax Number: 0844 846-8220 (Office)
Ground Capacity: 2,000
Seating Capacity: 250
Web Site: www.dtfc.co.uk

GENERAL INFORMATION
Car Parking: At the ground
Coach Parking: At the ground
Nearest Railway Station: Long Buckby (6 miles)
Club Shop: None
Opening Times: –
Telephone Nº: –

GROUND INFORMATION
Away Supporters' Entrances & Sections:
No usual segregation

ADMISSION INFO (2010/2011 PRICES)
Adult Standing: £6.00
Adult Seating: £6.00
Concessionary Standing: £4.00
Concessionary Seating: £4.00
Under-16s Standing/Seating: Free of charge
Programme Price: £1.00

DISABLED INFORMATION
Wheelchairs: Accommodated
Helpers: Admitted
Prices: Normal prices apply for the disabled and helpers
Disabled Toilets: –
Contact: 0844 846-8228 (Bookings are not necessary)

Travelling Supporters' Information:
Routes: Take the A45 to the western outskirts of Daventry near to Staverton Park Golf Club and, at the roundabout junction with the A425, cross over into Browns Road. The ground is on the left hand side of the road after approximately 200 yards.

HITCHIN TOWN FC

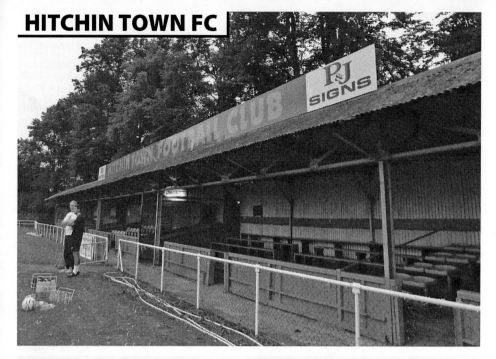

Founded: 1865   (Re-formed in 1928)
Former Names: Hitchin FC
Nickname: 'The Canaries'
Ground: Top Field, Fishponds Road, Hitchin, Hertfordshire   SG5 1NU
Record Attendance: 7,878 (1956)
Ground Capacity: 4,554   **Seating Capacity:** 500

Pitch Size: 114 × 78 yards
Colours: Yellow shirts with Green shorts
Telephone Nº: (01462) 434483 (Club)
Daytime Phone Nº: (01767) 315350
Matchday Phone Nº: (01462) 459028
Fax Number: (01462) 638718
Web site: www.hitchintownnfc.co.uk

GENERAL INFORMATION
Car Parking: Space for 200 cars at the ground
Coach Parking: At the ground
Nearest Railway Station: Hitchin (1 mile)
Club Shop: At the ground
Opening Times: Matchdays only
Telephone Nº: None

GROUND INFORMATION
Away Supporters' Entrances & Sections:
No usual segregation

ADMISSION INFO   (2010/2011 PRICES)
Adult Standing/Seating: £9.00
Concessionary Standing/Seating: £5.00
Under-17s Standing/Seating: £1.00
Programme Price: £2.00

DISABLED INFORMATION
Wheelchairs: 10 spaces are available by the Main Stand
Helpers: Admitted
Prices: Normal prices apply
Disabled Toilets: Available at rear of the Main Stand
Contact: (01462) 434483 or (01767) 315350 (Please book)

Travelling Supporters' Information:
Routes: Take A1(M) to Junction 8 and follow A602 signposted to Hitchin. At Three Moorhens roundabout, take 3rd exit onto A600 towards Bedford. At next roundabout go straight over onto one-way system, go straight over at traffic lights, turn right at next roundabout and the turnstiles are immediately on the left. The Car Park turning is 50 yards further on; Alternatively, take M1 to Junction 10 and follow well appointed signs to Hitchin via A505. On approach to Hitchin go straight over initial mini-roundabout, turn left at next roundabout and turnstiles are situated immediately on the left; By Train: From Hitchin Station turn right outside station approach and follow the road around the DIY store into Nightingale Road which leads past the Woolpack Pub to The Victoria. Take Bunyan Road at The Victoria which leads into Fishponds Road.

LEIGHTON TOWN FC

Founded: 1885
Former Names: Leighton United FC
Nickname: 'Reds'
Ground: Bell Close, Lake Street, Leighton Buzzard, LU7 1RX
Record Attendance: 1,522 (30th January 1993)

Colours: Red and White striped shirts with Red shorts
Telephone Nº: (01525) 373311
Ground Capacity: 2,800
Seating Capacity: 155
Web Site: www.leightontownfc.co.uk

GENERAL INFORMATION

Car Parking: At the ground
Coach Parking: At the ground
Nearest Railway Station: Leighton Buzzard (1 mile)
Club Shop: None
Opening Times: –
Telephone Nº: –

GROUND INFORMATION

Away Supporters' Entrances & Sections:
No usual segregation

ADMISSION INFO (2010/2011 PRICES)

Adult Standing/Seating: £8.00
Concessionary Standing/Seating: £5.00
Child Standing/Seating: £2.00
Programme Price: £1.50

DISABLED INFORMATION

Wheelchairs: Accommodated
Helpers: Admitted
Prices: Normal prices apply for the disabled and helpers
Disabled Toilets: None
Contact: (01525) 373311 (Bookings are not necessary)

Travelling Supporters' Information:
Routes: The ground is located by the side of the A4146 Leighton Buzzard to Hemel Hempstead road, approximately ¼ mile south of Leighton Town Centre. The entrance to the ground is located directly opposite the Morrison's Supermarket Petrol Station.

MARLOW FC

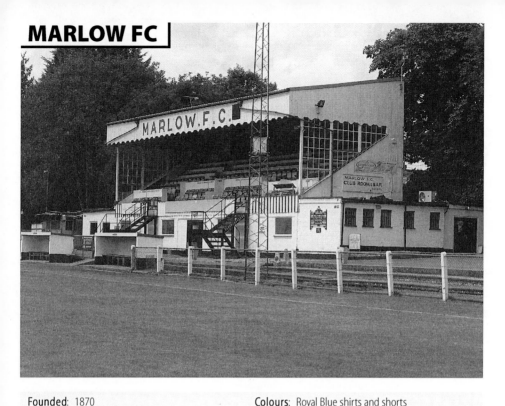

Founded: 1870
Former Names: Great Marlow FC
Nickname: 'The Blues'
Ground: Alfred Davies Memorial Ground, Oak Tree Road, Marlow   SL7 3ED
Record Attendance: 3,000 (1994)

Colours: Royal Blue shirts and shorts
Telephone Nº: (01628) 483970
Ground Capacity: 3,000
Seating Capacity: 250
Web Site: www.marlowfc.co.uk

GENERAL INFORMATION
Car Parking: At the ground
Coach Parking: At the ground
Nearest Railway Station: Marlow (¾ mile)
Club Shop: None
Opening Times: –
Telephone Nº: –

GROUND INFORMATION
Away Supporters' Entrances & Sections:
No usual segregation

ADMISSION INFO (2010/2011 PRICES)
Adult Standing: £8.00
Adult Seating: £8.00
Senior Citizen/Junior Standing: £4.00
Senior Citizen/Junior Seating: £4.00
Programme Price: £1.00

DISABLED INFORMATION
Wheelchairs: Accommodated
Helpers: Admitted
Prices: Normal prices apply for the disabled. Helpers are admitted free of charge
Disabled Toilets: None
Contact: (01628) 483970   (Bookings are necessary)

Travelling Supporters' Information:
Routes: Exit the M40 at Junction 4 and take the A404 towards Marlow. Take the first exit for the A4155, follow the A4155 towards Marlow and turn right immediately after the Esso service station called 'On The Run' into Maple Rise. Cross directly over the crossroads into Oak Tree Road and the ground can be found approximately on the left after approximately 100 yards.

NORTH GREENFORD UNITED FC

Founded: 1944
Former Names: None
Nickname: 'The Blues'
Ground: Berkeley Fields, Berkeley Avenue, Greenford   UB6 0NX
Record Attendance: 985

Colours: Blue and White shirts with Blue shorts
Telephone Nº: (020) 8422-8923
Ground Capacity: 2,000
Seating Capacity: 150
Web Site: www.northgreenfordunitedfc.co.uk

GENERAL INFORMATION

Car Parking: At the ground
Coach Parking: At the ground
Nearest Railway Station: Greenford (½ mile)
Nearest Tube Station: Greenford (½ mile)
Club Shop: None
Opening Times: –
Telephone Nº: –

GROUND INFORMATION

Away Supporters' Entrances & Sections:
No usual segregation

ADMISSION INFO (2010/2011 PRICES)

Adult Standing: £8.00
Adult Seating: £8.00
Senior Citizen/Junior Standing: £4.00
Senior Citizen/Junior Seating: £4.00
Programme Price: Included with admission

DISABLED INFORMATION

Wheelchairs: Accommodated
Helpers: Admitted
Prices: Concessionary prices are charged for the disabled and helpers
Disabled Toilets: Available
Contact: (020) 8422-8923   (Bookings are necessary)

Travelling Supporters' Information:
Routes: Exit the M25 at Junction 16 and take the M40 towards London. Continue into the A40 then exit at the Greenford Roundabout onto the A4127 heading into Greenford. Pass under the railway bridge and continue northwards along Greenford Road passing the Paradise Fields Shopping Complex. Turn right into Berkeley Avenue at the traffic lights opposite Glaxo and the entrance to the ground is at the bottom of the hill on the right.

NORTHWOOD FC

Founded: 1899
Former Names: None
Nickname: 'Woods'
Ground: Northwood Park, Chestnut Avenue, Northwood   HA6 1HR
Record Attendance: 1,642 (vs Chelsea, 1997)
Pitch Size: 118 × 80 yards

Colours: Red shirts and shorts
Telephone N°: (01923) 827148
Ground Capacity: 3,075
Seating Capacity: 308
Web site: www.northwoodfc.com

GENERAL INFORMATION
Car Parking: 100 spaces available at the ground
Coach Parking: In Chestnut Avenue
Nearest Underground Station: Northwood Hills (½ mile)
Club Shop: At the ground
Opening Times: Matchdays only
Telephone N°: None

GROUND INFORMATION
Away Supporters' Entrances & Sections:
No usual segregation

ADMISSION INFO (2010/2011 PRICES)
Adult Standing/Seating: £8.00
Concessionary Standing/Seating: £4.00
Under-16s Standing/Seating: Free of charge
Programme Price: £1.50

DISABLED INFORMATION
Wheelchairs: Accommodated
Helpers: Admitted
Prices: Normal prices apply
Disabled Toilets: None
Contact: (01923) 827148   (Bookings are not necessary)

Travelling Supporters' Information:
Routes: The ground is situated just off the Pinner to Rickmansworth road (A404) in Northwood. Approaching from Pinner turn left into Chestnut Avenue by the large grey railway bridge for the ground.

RUGBY TOWN FC

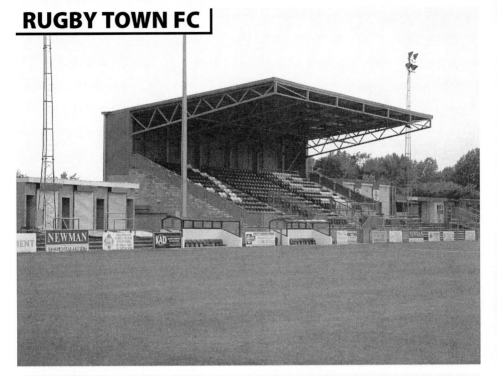

Founded: 1956
Former Names: Glebe Rangers FC, New Bilton Juniors FC, Valley Sports FC, Valley Sports Rugby FC, V.S.Rugby FC and Rugby United FC
Nickname: 'The Valley'
Ground: Butlin Road, Rugby CV21 3SD
Record Attendance: 3,961 (1984)
Pitch Size: 110 × 72 yards

Colours: Sky Blue shirts with White shorts
Office Telephone Nº: (01788) 866920
Correspondence: Melbros House, Great Central Way, Rugby CV21 3XH
Ground Capacity: 6,000
Seating Capacity: 740
Web site: www.rugbytownfc.com

GENERAL INFORMATION
Car Parking: At the ground
Coach Parking: At the ground
Nearest Railway Station: Rugby (1 mile)
Nearest Bus Station: Rugby
Club Shop: At the ground
Opening Times: Matchdays only
Telephone Nº: (01788) 844806

GROUND INFORMATION
Away Supporters' Entrances & Sections:
No usual segregation

ADMISSION INFO (2010/2011 PRICES)
Adult Standing: £8.00
Adult Seating: £8.00
Senior Citizen/Junior Standing: £4.00
Senior Citizen/Junior Seating: £4.00
Programme Price: £2.00

DISABLED INFORMATION
Wheelchairs: Accommodated
Helpers: Admitted
Prices: Normal prices apply
Disabled Toilets: Available
Contact: (01788) 866920

Travelling Supporters' Information:
Routes: Exit the M6 at Junction 1 and take the A426 into Rugby. Cross the railway and turn left from Newbold Road into Wood Street. Take the second turning on the right into Railway Terrace then turn left at the end along the B5414 Clifton Road. Butlin Road is about ½ mile along, near the Golf Course.

SLOUGH TOWN FC

Slough Town FC are groundsharing with Beaconsfield SYCOB FC during the 2010-2011 season.

Founded: 1890
Former Names: Slough FC and Slough United FC
Nickname: 'The Rebels'
Ground: Holloways Park, Slough Road, Beaconsfield HP9 2SE
Record Attendance: 8,000

Colours: Amber shirts with Navy Blue shorts
Contact Telephone Nº: 07989 434371
Ground Capacity: 3,500
Seating Capacity: 200
Web site: www.sloughtownfc.net
E-mail: secretary@sloughtownfc.net

GENERAL INFORMATION

Car Parking: At the ground
Coach Parking: At the ground
Nearest Railway Station: Beaconsfield (2½ miles)
Club Shop: None
Opening Times: –
Telephone Nº: –

GROUND INFORMATION

Away Supporters' Entrances & Sections:
No usual segregation

ADMISSION INFO (2010/2011 PRICES)

Adult Standing: £8.00
Adult Seating: £8.00
Child/Senior Citizen Standing: £4.00
Child/Senior Citizen Seating: £4.00
Programme Price: £1.50

DISABLED INFORMATION

Wheelchairs: Accommodated
Helpers: Admitted
Prices: Normal prices apply for the disabled and helpers
Disabled Toilets: Available
Contact: 07989 434371 (Bookings are not necessary)

Travelling Supporters' Information:
Routes: Exit the M40 at Junction 2 and head into the Beaconsfield Motorway Service area. In the services, follow the signs for Beaconsfield SYCOB, crossing the A355 and heading back towards the M40. After approximately 150 yards turn left into the ground and the car park and Clubhouse are on the right after 200 yards.

SOHAM TOWN RANGERS FC

Founded: 1947
Former Names: Soham Town FC
Nickname: 'The Greens'
Ground: Julius Martin Lane, Soham, Ely   CB7 5EQ
Record Attendance: 3,000 (1963)

Colours: Shirts and shorts are Green with White trim
Telephone Nº: (01353) 720732
Ground Capacity: 2,000
Seating Capacity: 250
Web Site: www.webteams.co.uk/sohamtownrangersfc

GENERAL INFORMATION
Car Parking: At the ground
Coach Parking: At the ground
Nearest Railway Station: Ely (5 miles)
Club Shop: None
Opening Times: –
Telephone Nº: –

GROUND INFORMATION
Away Supporters' Entrances & Sections:
No usual segregation

ADMISSION INFO (2010/2011 PRICES)
Adult Standing: £7.00
Adult Seating: £7.00
Senior Citizen/Junior Standing: £4.00
Senior Citizen/Junior Seating: £4.00
Programme Price: £1.50

DISABLED INFORMATION
Wheelchairs: Accommodated
Helpers: Admitted
Prices: Normal prices apply for the disabled and helpers
Disabled Toilets: None
Contact: (01353) 720732   (Bookings are not necessary)

Travelling Supporters' Information:
Routes: Soham is located just to the west of the A142, between Newmarket and Ely. Exit the A142 at the roundabout just to the north of Soham and follow the road named 'The Shade' into town. Continue along this road into Townsend, follow round the bend then turn right into Julius Martin Lane. The ground is on the left hand side towards the end of the lane.

UXBRIDGE FC

Founded: 1871
Former Names: Uxbridge Town FC
Nickname: 'The Reds'
Ground: Honeycroft, Horton Road, West Drayton, UB7 8HX
Record Attendance: 1,000 (1981)

Colours: Red shirts with White shorts
Telephone Nº: (01895) 443557
Fax Number: (01895) 445830
Ground Capacity: 3,770
Seating Capacity: 339
Web Site: www.uxbridgefc.co.uk

GENERAL INFORMATION
Car Parking: At the ground and also street parking
Coach Parking: At the ground
Nearest Railway Station: West Drayton (½ mile)
Nearest Tube Station: Uxbridge (3 miles)
Club Shop: None
Opening Times: –
Telephone Nº: –

GROUND INFORMATION
Away Supporters' Entrances & Sections:
No usual segregation

ADMISSION INFO (2010/2011 PRICES)
Adult Standing: £8.00
Adult Seating: £8.00
Senior Citizen/Junior Standing: £4.00
Senior Citizen/Junior Seating: £4.00
Programme Price: £1.50

DISABLED INFORMATION
Wheelchairs: Accommodated (2 spaces available only)
Helpers: Admitted
Prices: Normal prices apply for the disabled. Helpers are admitted free of charge
Disabled Toilets: Available
Contact: (01895) 445830 (Bookings are necessary)

Travelling Supporters' Information:
Routes: Exit the M4 at Junction 4 and follow the A408 northwards. After passing Heathpark Golf Course and crossing the railway line and the canal, take the slip road before the flyover onto Horton Road. Take the second exit at Stockley Park Roundabout continuing on Horton Road and entrance to the ground is on the right after a short distance, just before the bend in the road.

WOODFORD UNITED FC

Founded: 1946
Former Names: None
Nickname: 'The Reds'
Ground: Byfield Road, Woodford Halse, Daventry, NN11 3TR
Record Attendance: 1,500

Colours: Red shirts and shorts
Telephone N°: (01327) 263734
Fax Number: (01327) 263734
Ground Capacity: 3,000
Seating Capacity: 252
Web Site: www.woodford-united.co.uk

GENERAL INFORMATION
Car Parking: At the ground
Coach Parking: At the ground
Nearest Railway Station: Banbury (12 miles)
Club Shop: None
Opening Times: –
Telephone N°: –

GROUND INFORMATION
Away Supporters' Entrances & Sections:
No usual segregation

ADMISSION INFO (2010/2011 PRICES)
Adult Standing: £7.00
Adult Seating: £7.00
Senior Citizen/Junior Standing: £4.00
Senior Citizen/Junior Seating: £4.00
Programme Price: £1.50

DISABLED INFORMATION
Wheelchairs: Accommodated
Helpers: Admitted
Prices: Concessionary prices are charged for the disabled and helpers
Disabled Toilets: Available
Contact: (01327) 263734 (Bookings are not necessary)

Travelling Supporters' Information:
Routes: Take the A361 south from Daventry or north from Banbury and head to Byfield village. At the dual mini-roundabouts in Byfield, turn off the A361 and head east towards Hinton along Woodford Road into Byfield Road. Continue along Byfield Road, passing through Hinton and the ground is on the left hand side of the road just after passing the Industrial Estate.

THE ZAMARETTO LEAGUE
DIVISION ONE SOUTH & WEST

Secretary Jason Mills

Correspondence
secretary@southern-football-league.co.uk

Web Site www.southern-football-league.co.uk

Clubs for the 2010/2011 Season

ABINGDON UNITED FC

Founded: 1946
Former Names: None
Nickname: 'The Us'
Ground: The North Court, North Court Road, Abingdon   OX14 1PL
Record Attendance: 2,000 (vs Oxford United – 2002)

Colours: Yellow shirts and shorts
Telephone Nº: (01235) 203203
Fax Number: (01235) 202124
Ground Capacity: 2,000
Seating Capacity: 158
Web Site: www.abingdonunitedfc.co.uk

GENERAL INFORMATION

Car Parking: At the ground
Coach Parking: At the ground
Nearest Railway Station: Radley (2¼ miles)
Club Shop: None
Opening Times: –
Telephone Nº: –

GROUND INFORMATION

Away Supporters' Entrances & Sections:
No usual segregation

ADMISSION INFO (2010/2011 PRICES)

Adult Standing: £6.00
Adult Seating: £6.00
Senior Citizen/Junior Standing: £3.00
Senior Citizen/Junior Seating: £3.00
Programme Price: £1.50

DISABLED INFORMATION

Wheelchairs: Accommodated
Helpers: Admitted
Prices: Normal prices apply for the disabled and helpers
Disabled Toilets: Available
Contact: (01235) 203203   (Bookings are not necessary)

Travelling Supporters' Information:
Routes: Take the A34 southwards from Oxford and exit onto the A4183 just to the north of Abingdon. Continue into Abingdon along the A4183 (Oxford Road), go straight on at the roundabout then take the 6th turning on the right into Northcourt Road. The entrance to the ground is then immediately on the left.

AFC TOTTON

The photograph was taken while the new ground was still under construction. This new ground is scheduled to open in October 2010. Prior to this date, games will be played at Testwood Park, situated in Testwood Place, off Testwood Lane approximately 1 mile further down Salisbury Road. (Sat Nav for Testwood Park: SO40 3BE)

Founded: 1886
Former Names: Totton FC
Nickname: 'The Stags'
Ground: Little Testwood Farm, Salisbury Road, Totton, Southampton
Record Attendance: Not applicable as the ground has yet to host a game

Colours: Blue shirts and shorts
Telephone Nº: (023) 8086-8981 (Testwood Park number which may change for the new ground)
Ground Capacity: 2,000
Seating Capacity: 500
Web Site: www.afctotton.com
Contact E-mail: secretary@afctotton.com

GENERAL INFORMATION

Car Parking: At the Industrial Park adjacent to the ground
Coach Parking: At the ground
Nearest Railway Station: Totton (1½ miles)
Club Shop: At the ground
Opening Times: To be announced
Telephone Nº: –

GROUND INFORMATION

Away Supporters' Entrances & Sections:
No usual segregation

ADMISSION INFO (2010/2011 PRICES)

Adult Standing: £8.00
Adult Seating: £8.00
Senior Citizen/Junior Standing: £4.00
Senior Citizen/Junior Seating: £4.00
Programme Price: £1.50

DISABLED INFORMATION

Wheelchairs: Accommodated
Helpers: Admitted
Prices: Normal prices apply for the disabled and helpers
Disabled Toilets: Available
Contact: Sean McGlead, c/o Club (Bookings are necessary)

Travelling Supporters' Information:
Routes: Exit the M27 at Junction 2 and head south on the A326. Almost immediately, take the slip road and turn left to join the A36 heading into Totton. The ground is located on the left hand side of the road after approximately ¾ mile, just before the roundabout for Calmore Industrial Park. Spectators travelling by car should turn left at this roundabout and can use the car park of Mansell Construction Services Ltd. which is immediately on the right after entering the Industrial Park.

ALMONDSBURY TOWN FC

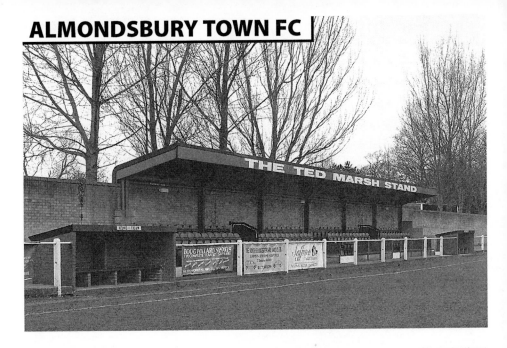

Founded: 1897
Former Names: Almondsbury Greenway FC and Almondsbury Picksons FC
Nickname: 'The Almonds'
Ground: Oaklands Park, Almondsbury, Bristol, BS32 4AG
Record Attendance: 2,100 (1989/90 season)

Colours: Sky Blue and White striped shirts with Navy Blue shorts
Telephone Nº: (01454) 612740
Fax Number: (0117) 969-9413
Ground Capacity: 2,500
Seating Capacity: 152
Web: www.pitchero.com/clubs/almondsburytownfc

GENERAL INFORMATION

Car Parking: At the ground
Coach Parking: At the ground
Nearest Railway Station: Parkway (4 miles)
Club Shop: At the ground
Opening Times: Matchdays only
Telephone Nº: (01454) 612740

GROUND INFORMATION

Away Supporters' Entrances & Sections:
No usual segregation

ADMISSION INFO (2010/2011 PRICES)

Adult Standing: £7.00
Adult Seating: £7.00
Senior Citizen/Junior Standing: £4.00
Senior Citizen/Junior Seating: £4.00
Note: Under-10s are admitted free of charge when accompanying a paying adult
Programme Price: £1.50

DISABLED INFORMATION

Wheelchairs: Accommodated
Helpers: Admitted
Prices: Concessionary prices are charged for disabled fans and helpers
Disabled Toilets: Available
Contact: 07903 655723   (Bookings are necessary)

Travelling Supporters' Information:
Routes: Exit the M5 at Junction 16 and head North on the A38 Gloucester Road (3rd exit at the top of the slip road). Take the first turning on the left after approximately 100 yards and the ground is on the right hand side at the end of the road.

ANDOVER FC

Founded: 1883
Former Names: None
Nickname: 'The Lions'
Ground: The Portway Stadium, West Portway Industrial Estate, Andover   SP10 3LF
Record Attendance: 1,100

Colours: Red and Black shirts with Black shorts
Telephone Nº: (01264) 351302
Ground Capacity: 3,000
Seating Capacity: 250
Web Site: www.andover-fc.co.uk

GENERAL INFORMATION

Car Parking: At the ground
Coach Parking: At the ground
Nearest Railway Station: Andover (2 miles)
Club Shop: None
Opening Times: –
Telephone Nº: –

GROUND INFORMATION

Away Supporters' Entrances & Sections:
No usual segregation

ADMISSION INFO (2010/2011 PRICES)

Adult Standing: £8.00
Adult Seating: £8.00
Senior Citizen Standing: £4.00
Senior Citizen Seating: £4.00
Under-16s: Admitted free of charge for League games
Programme Price: £1.00

DISABLED INFORMATION

Wheelchairs: Accommodated
Helpers: Admitted
Prices: Normal prices apply for the disabled and helpers
Disabled Toilets: Available
Contact: (01264) 351302   (Bookings are not necessary)

Travelling Supporters' Information:
Routes: The ground is located in the West Portway Industrial Estate, on the western outskirts of Andover. Take the A303 to the interchange with the A343 and A342 Weyhill Road. At the roundabout exit onto the A343 heading northwards then take the first exit at the next roundabout into West Portway. The entrance to the ground is then on the right hand side of the road.

BIDEFORD FC

Founded: 1949
Former Names: Bideford Town FC
Nickname: 'The Robins'
Ground: The Sports Ground, Kingsley Road,
Bideford   EX39 2NG
Record Attendance: 6,000

Colours: Red shirts and shorts
Telephone Nº: (01237) 474974
Ground Capacity: 6,000
Seating Capacity: 375
Web Site: www.bidefordafc.co.uk

GENERAL INFORMATION
Car Parking: At the ground
Coach Parking: In Kingsley Road
Nearest Railway Station: Barnstaple (9½ miles)
Club Shop: At the ground
Opening Times: Matchdays only from 2.00pm to kick-off
Telephone Nº: –

GROUND INFORMATION
Away Supporters' Entrances & Sections:
No usual segregation

ADMISSION INFO (2010/2011 PRICES)
Adult Standing: £7.00
Adult Seating: £7.00
Senior Citizen/Junior Standing: £4.00
Senior Citizen/Junior Seating: £4.00
Programme Price: £1.00

DISABLED INFORMATION
Wheelchairs: Accommodated
Helpers: Admitted
Prices: Normal prices apply for the disabled and helpers
Disabled Toilets: Available
Contact: (01237) 474974   (Bookings are necessary)

Travelling Supporters' Information:
Routes: Take the A39 over the high level Torridge Bridge then turn left at the roundabout towards Bideford along Kingsley Road. Follow this road down towards the River Quayside and the ground is on the right hand side across the road from the Morrisons Supermarket.

BISHOP'S CLEEVE FC

Founded: 1905
Former Names: None
Nickname: 'The Villagers'
Ground: Kayte Lane, Bishop's Cleeve, Cheltenham, GL52 3PD
Record Attendance: 1,300 (vs Newport County in July 2006)

Colours: Blue shirts and shorts
Telephone N°: (01242) 676166
Fax Number: (01386) 750227
Ground Capacity: 1,500
Seating Capacity: 50
Web Site: www.webteams.co.uk/bishopscleevefc

GENERAL INFORMATION
Car Parking: At the ground
Coach Parking: Inside the ground
Nearest Railway Station: Cheltenham Spa (4 miles)
Club Shop: At the ground
Opening Times: –
Telephone N°: –

GROUND INFORMATION
Away Supporters' Entrances & Sections:
No usual segregation

ADMISSION INFO (2010/2011 PRICES)
Adult Standing: £6.00
Adult Seating: £6.00
Senior Citizen/Junior Standing: £4.00
Senior Citizen/Junior Seating: £4.00
Programme Price: £1.00

DISABLED INFORMATION
Wheelchairs: Accommodated
Helpers: Admitted
Prices: Concessionary prices are charged for the disabled and helpers
Disabled Toilets: Available
Contact: (01242) 676166 (Bookings are not necessary)

Travelling Supporters' Information:
Routes: The ground is situated off the A435 Cheltenham to Bishop's Cleeve road just to the south of Bishop's Cleeve. Head north on the A435 from Cheltenham passing the Racecourse then take the first turn on the right into Southam Lane. Take the next left into Kayte Lane and the ground is on the left after approximately 500 yards.

BRIDGWATER TOWN FC 1984

Founded: 1898 (Re-formed several times since)
Former Names: Bridgwater Town FC
Nickname: 'The Robins'
Ground: Fairfax Park, College Way, Bath Road, Bridgwater   TA6 4TZ
Record Attendance: 1,112 (26th February 1997)

Colours: Red shirts with White shorts
Telephone Nº: (01278) 446899
Fax Number: (01278) 446899
Ground Capacity: 2,500
Seating Capacity: 318
Web Site: www.bridgwatertownfc1984.co.uk

GENERAL INFORMATION
Car Parking: 150 spaces available at the ground
Coach Parking: At the ground
Nearest Railway Station: Bridgwater (¾ mile)
Club Shop: At the ground
Opening Times: Matchdays only
Telephone Nº: 07849 510210

GROUND INFORMATION
Away Supporters' Entrances & Sections:
No usual segregation

ADMISSION INFO (2010/2011 PRICES)
Adult Standing: £8.00
Adult Seating: £8.00
Senior Citizen Standing: £6.00
Senior Citizen Seating: £6.00
Under-16s Standing/Seating: £2.00
Programme Price: £1.50

DISABLED INFORMATION
Wheelchairs: Accommodated
Helpers: Admitted
Prices: Normal prices apply for the disabled. Helpers are admitted free of charge
Disabled Toilets: Available
Contact: (01278) 446899   (Bookings are preferred)

Travelling Supporters' Information:
Routes: Exit the M5 at Junction 23 and turn left onto the A39 heading towards Glastonbury. Continue over the hill until the junction just past Knowle Hall (on the left). Turn right towards Bridgwater (A39), pass over the motorway and continue along Bath Road. Pass the old Innova factory on the right and slow down as the road narrows with terraced houses on both sides. Take the turning immediately on the left (signposted Bridgwater College) by the Bridgwater & Albion RFC Ground, just before crossing the railway bridge. In College Way, take the second turning on the right into the ground just before the College gates.

BROMSGROVE ROVERS FC

Note: The club were excluded from the League after the season's fixtures were prepared and will not play during 2010/11 unless a successful appeal is lodged within the prescribed time.

Founded: 1885
Former Names: None
Nickname: 'The Rovers'
Ground: Victoria Ground, Birmingham Road, Bromsgrove   B61 0DR
Record Attendance: 7,563 (1957/58 season)
Pitch Size: 110 × 72 yards

Colours: Green & White striped shirts, Black shorts
Telephone Nº: (01527) 876949
Fax Number: (01527) 876265
Ground Capacity: 4,893
Seating Capacity: 394
Web site: None

GENERAL INFORMATION
Car Parking: 200 spaces available at the ground
Coach Parking: By Police Direction
Nearest Railway Station: Bromsgrove (1½ miles)
Nearest Bus Station: 500 yards
Club Shop: At the ground
Opening Times: Weekdays 9.00am to 1.00pm and also at all home matches
Telephone Nº: (01527) 876949

GROUND INFORMATION
Away Supporters' Entrances & Sections:
No usual segregation

DISABLED INFORMATION
Wheelchairs: 6 spaces are available (more if necessary) outside of the Police Control Room
Helpers: Please phone the club for information
Prices: Please phone the club for information
Disabled Toilets: Available
Contact: (01527) 876949   (Bookings are necessary)

Travelling Supporters' Information:
Routes: From the North: Exit the M42 at Junction 1 and follow the A38 towards Bromsgrove. Once in Bromsgrove, follow the Town Centre signs at the traffic lights. Victoria Ground is approximately 2 minutes away next to Clark's Motor Services on the right hand side; From the South: Exit the M5 at Junction 4 onto the A38. Then as above.

CINDERFORD TOWN FC

Unfortunately, no ground photograph
for Cinderford Town FC was available
at the time of going to press.

Founded: 1922
Former Names: None
Nickname: 'The Foresters'
Ground: The Causeway, Edge Hills Road, Cinderford, GL14 2QH
Record Attendance: 4,850 (1955/56 season)

Colours: Black and White striped shirts, Black shorts
Telephone Nº: (01594) 827147
Fax Number: (01594) 835945
Ground Capacity: 3,500
Seating Capacity: 250
Web Site: www.pitchero.com/clubs/cinderfordtown

GENERAL INFORMATION
Car Parking: At the ground
Coach Parking: At the ground
Nearest Railway Station: Lydney (11½ miles)
Club Shop: At the ground
Opening Times: Matchdays only
Telephone Nº: –

GROUND INFORMATION
Away Supporters' Entrances & Sections:
No usual segregation

ADMISSION INFO (2010/2011 PRICES)
Adult Standing: £6.00
Adult Seating: £6.00
Senior Citizen/Junior Standing: £3.00
Senior Citizen/Junior Seating: £3.00
Under-16s Standing/Seating: £1.00
Programme Price: £1.00

DISABLED INFORMATION
Wheelchairs: Accommodated
Helpers: Admitted
Prices: Normal prices apply for the disabled and helpers
Disabled Toilets: None
Contact: (01594) 827147   (Bookings are not necessary)

Travelling Supporters' Information:
Routes: Take the A48 southwards from Gloucester to Elton and join the A4151. Pass through Littledean then turn right into the High Street and continue along as the road becomes 'The Ruffitt' following it into Cinderford. At the junction turn into Causeway Road and Edge Hills Road is the 2nd turning on the left. The entrance to the ground is then on the left after the bend in the road.

CLEVEDON TOWN FC

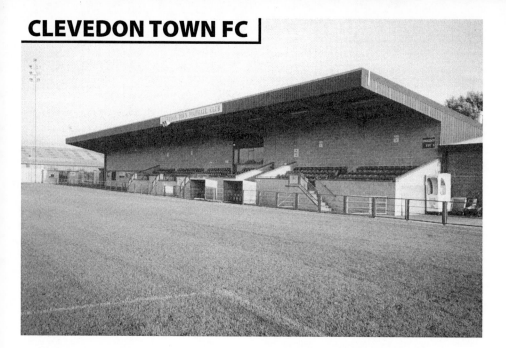

Founded: 1880
Former Names: None
Nickname: 'The Seasiders'
Ground: Hand Stadium, Davis Lane, Clevedon, BS21 6TG
Record Attendance: 3,264
Pitch Size: 100 × 70 yards

Colours: Blue and White striped shirts, Blue shorts
Telephone Nº: (01275) 341641
Office Phone Nº: (01275) 871600
Fax Number: (01275) 871601
Ground Capacity: 3,650
Seating Capacity: 300
Web site: www.clevedontownafc.co.uk

GENERAL INFORMATION
Car Parking: 240 spaces available at the ground
Coach Parking: 6 spaces available at the ground
Nearest Railway Station: Yatton
Nearest Bus Station: Bristol
Club Shop: At the ground
Opening Times: Matchdays only
Telephone Nº: (01275) 871600

GROUND INFORMATION
Away Supporters' Entrances:
No usual segregation

ADMISSION INFO (2010/2011 PRICES)
Adult Standing: £8.00
Adult Seating: £8.00
Child Standing: £1.00
Child Seating: £1.00
Senior Citizen Standing: £5.00
Senior Citizen Seating: £5.00
Programme Price: £1.50

DISABLED INFORMATION
Wheelchairs: Accommodated
Helpers: Admitted
Prices: Normal prices apply
Disabled Toilets: Available
Contact: (01275) 341641   (Bookings are not necessary)

Travelling Supporters' Information:
Routes: Exit the M5 at Junction 20 and follow signs for The Hand Stadium. Take the 1st left into Central Way (at the traffic island just after the motorway), take 1st left at the mini-roundabout into Kenn Road then 2nd left into Davis Lane. The ground is ½ mile on the right; From Bristol: Take the B3130 to Clevedon then turn left into Court Lane (opposite Clevedon Court) then turn right after 1 mile and the ground is on the left.

FROME TOWN FC

Founded: 1904
Former Names: None
Nickname: 'The Robins'
Ground: Aldersmith Stadium, Badgers Hill, Berkley Road, Frome   BA11 2EH
Record Attendance: 8,000 (1954)

Colours: Red shirts and shorts
Telephone Nº: (01373) 464087
Fax Number: (01373) 464087
Ground Capacity: 2,000
Seating Capacity: 150
Web Site: www.frometownfc.co.uk

GENERAL INFORMATION
Car Parking: At the ground
Coach Parking: At the ground
Nearest Railway Station: Frome (1 mile)
Club Shop: At the ground
Opening Times: Matchdays only
Telephone Nº: –

GROUND INFORMATION
Away Supporters' Entrances & Sections:
No usual segregation

ADMISSION INFO (2010/2011 PRICES)
Adult Standing/Seating: £8.00
Senior Citizen/Youth Standing/Seating: 5.00
Under-17s Standing/Seating: 2.00
Note: Under-12s are admitted free when with a paying adult
Programme Price: £1.50

DISABLED INFORMATION
Wheelchairs: Accommodated
Helpers: Admitted
Prices: Normal prices apply for the disabled and helpers
Disabled Toilets: None
Contact: (01373) 464087   (Bookings are necessary)

Travelling Supporters' Information:
Routes: Take the A36 southwards from Bath and, after passing Beckington, join the A361 heading towards Frome. At the next roundabout, join the B3090 and continue into Frome from the north. Turn left into Berkley Road shortly after passing the Cricket Ground on the left and Aldersmith Stadium is on the right hand side after a short distance.

GOSPORT BOROUGH FC

Founded: 1944
Former Names: Gosport Borough Athletic FC
Nickname: 'The Boro'
Ground: GHS Stadium, Privett Park, Privett Road, Gosport PO12 3SX
Record Attendance: 4,770 (1951)

Colours: Yellow shirts with Navy Blue shorts
Telephone Nº: (023) 9250-1042
Fax Number: (01329) 235961
Ground Capacity: 4,500
Seating Capacity: 450
Web Site: www.gosportboroughfc.com

GENERAL INFORMATION
Car Parking: At the ground
Coach Parking: At the ground
Nearest Railway Station: Fareham (5½ miles)
Club Shop: At the ground
Opening Times: Matchdays only
Telephone Nº: –

GROUND INFORMATION
Away Supporters' Entrances & Sections:
No usual segregation

ADMISSION INFO (2010/2011 PRICES)
Adult Standing: £8.00
Adult Seating: £8.00
Senior Citizen Standing: £4.00
Senior Citizen Seating: £4.00
Note: Under-15s are admitted free of charge when accompanied by a paying adult
Programme Price: £1.50

DISABLED INFORMATION
Wheelchairs: Accommodated
Helpers: Admitted
Prices: Normal prices apply for the disabled and helpers
Disabled Toilets: Available
Contact: (023) 9250-1042 (Bookings are not necessary)

Travelling Supporters' Information:
Routes: Exit the M27 at Junction 11 and follow take the A27 Eastern Way towards Gosport. Turn left at the roundabout to join the A32 Gosport Road and head south into Gosport. Continue along the A32 as it becomes Fareham Road then, at the second roundabout in a junction with two roundabouts, take the 3rd exit (signposted Alverstoke, Stokes Bay, Privett Park) into Military Road. Continue straight down this road, pass the playing fields on the left, then turn left at the roundabout into Privett Road. The entrance to the ground is the 4th turning on the left, just after the junction with Privett Place.

HUNGERFORD TOWN FC

Unfortunately, no ground photograph
for Hungerford Town FC was available
at the time of going to press.

Founded: 1886
Former Names: None
Nickname: 'The Crusaders'
Ground: Bulpit Lane, Hungerford   RG17 0AY
Record Attendance: 1,684 (1988/89 season)

Colours: White shirts with Blue shorts
Telephone Nº: (01488) 682939
Fax Number: (01793) 836550
Ground Capacity: 2,500
Seating Capacity: 170
Web Site: www.hungerfordtownfootballclub.co.uk

GENERAL INFORMATION

Car Parking: At the ground
Coach Parking: At the ground
Nearest Railway Station: Hungerford (½ mile)
Club Shop: At the ground
Opening Times: Matchdays only
Telephone Nº: –

GROUND INFORMATION

Away Supporters' Entrances & Sections:
No usual segregation

ADMISSION INFO (2010/2011 PRICES)

Adult Standing: £8.00
Adult Seating: £8.00
Senior Citizen/Junior Standing: £4.50
Senior Citizen/Junior Seating: £4.50
Programme Price: £1.00

DISABLED INFORMATION

Wheelchairs: Accommodated
Helpers: Admitted
Prices: Normal prices apply for the disabled and helpers
Disabled Toilets: Available
Contact: (01488) 682939   (Bookings are not necessary)

Travelling Supporters' Information:
Routes: Exit the M4 at Junction 14 and take the A338 towards Hungerford. Upon reaching Hungerford, turn right at the roundabout onto the A4 Bath Road, turn left at the next rounabout into Charnham Street then turn left again into Bridge Street (A338). The road becomes the High Street and pass under the railway line, carry straight on over three mini-roundabouts then take the next left into Priory Road. Continue to the end of the street and continue left into Priory Road then take the 3rd turning on the left into Bulpit Lane. The entrance to the ground is on the left shortly after crossing the junction with Priory Avenue.

MANGOTSFIELD UNITED FC

Founded: 1888 (Reformed 1951)
Former Names: Mangotsfield FC
Nickname: 'The Field'
Ground: Cossham Street, Mangotsfield, Bristol, BS16 9EN
Record Attendance: 2,386 (vs Bath City 1977-78)

Colours: Sky Blue shirts with Maroon shorts
Telephone Nº: (0117) 956-0119
Fax Number: (0117) 956-7424
Ground Capacity: 2,500
Seating Capacity: 300
Web site: mangos.freehosting.net

GENERAL INFORMATION

Car Parking: 80 spaces available at the ground
Coach Parking: At the nearby Cleeve Rugby Ground
Nearest Railway Station: Bristol Parkway (5 miles)
Nearest Bus Station: Central Bristol (7 miles)
Club Shop: At the ground
Opening Times: Matchdays only
Telephone Nº: (0117) 956-0119

GROUND INFORMATION

Away Supporters' Entrances & Sections:
No usual segregation

ADMISSION INFO (2010/2011 PRICES)

Adult Standing/Seating: £8.00
Senior Citizen Standing/Seating: £5.00
Under-16s Standing/Seating: £3.00
Programme Price: £1.50

DISABLED INFORMATION

Wheelchairs: Accommodated at the front of the stand
Helpers: Admitted
Prices: Standard prices apply
Disabled Toilets: Available in the Clubhouse
Contact: (0117) 956-0119 (Bookings are necessary)

Travelling Supporters' Information:
Routes: Exit the M32 at Junction 1 and follow the A4174 Ring Road through the traffic lights at the crossroads. At the first roundabout turn left and continue on the A4174. Carry straight on at the second roundabout then turn right at the third roundabout onto the Westerleigh Road, passing the Beefeater pub on the right and the Shell Garage on the left. Cross the mini-roundabout then turn left at the traffic lights into Blackhorse Road. Continue across another mini-roundabout into Richmond Road then turn left at the T-junction with St. James Street opposite the Red Lion. Continue for approximately 150 yards then take the 2nd turning on the left into Cossham Street. The ground is approximately 400 yards down the road on the right.

NORTH LEIGH FC

Founded: 1908
Former Names: None
Nickname: 'The Millers'
Ground: Eynsham Hall Sports Park, North Leigh, Witney   OX29 6PN
Record Attendance: 426 (16th October 2004)

Colours: Yellow shirts with Black shorts
Telephone N°: (01993) 881427
Ground Capacity: 2,000
Seating Capacity: 175
Web Site: www.pitchero.com/clubs/northleighfc

GENERAL INFORMATION

Car Parking: At the ground
Coach Parking: At the ground
Nearest Railway Station: Hanborough (2½ miles)
Club Shop: None
Opening Times: –
Telephone N°: –

GROUND INFORMATION

Away Supporters' Entrances & Sections:
No usual segregation

ADMISSION INFO (2010/2011 PRICES)

Adult Standing: £7.00
Adult Seating: £7.00
Senior Citizen/Junior Standing: £3.50
Senior Citizen/Junior Seating: £3.50
Under-14s Standing/Seating: Free of charge
Programme Price: £1.00

DISABLED INFORMATION

Wheelchairs: Accommodated
Helpers: Admitted
Prices: Normal prices apply for the disabled. Helpers are admitted free of charge
Disabled Toilets: Available
Contact: (01993) 881427   (Bookings are not necessary)

Travelling Supporters' Information:
Routes: Exit the M40 at Junction 9 and take the A34 towards Oxford. After about 5 miles take the slip road to the Peartree Interchange and head northwards on the A44 signposted for Woodstock & Evesham. Continue along the A44 and, shortly after passing Oxford Airport on the right, then turn left onto the A4095 at the roundabout. Continue down the A4095 passing through Long Hanborough and the entrance to the ground is located on the left as you enter North Leigh village.

PAULTON ROVERS FC

Founded: 1881
Former Names: None
Nickname: 'The Rovers'
Ground: Athletic Ground, Winterfield Road, Paulton, Bristol BS39 7RF
Record Attendance: 2,070 (vs Norwich City, 2009)

Colours: Shirts and shorts are White with Maroon trim
Telephone N°: (01761) 412907
Ground Capacity: 2,200
Seating Capacity: 253
Web Site: www.paultonrovers.co.uk

GENERAL INFORMATION
Car Parking: At the ground
Coach Parking: At the ground
Nearest Railway Station: Oldfield Park (9½ miles)
Club Shop: None
Opening Times: –
Telephone N°: –

GROUND INFORMATION
Away Supporters' Entrances & Sections:
No usual segregation

ADMISSION INFO (2010/2011 PRICES)
Adult Standing: £7.00
Adult Seating: £7.00
Senior Citizen/Junior Standing: £4.00
Senior Citizen/Junior Seating: £4.00
Note: Under-16s are admitted free of charge when accompanying a paying adult
Programme Price: £2.00

DISABLED INFORMATION
Wheelchairs: Accommodated
Helpers: Admitted
Prices: Normal prices apply for the disabled. Helpers are admitted free of charge
Disabled Toilets: Available in the Clubhouse
Contact: (01761) 412907   (Bookings are not necessary)

Travelling Supporters' Information:
Routes: Paulton is located to the south of Bristol just to the east of the A37. Take the A37 to Farrington Gurney and turn off onto the A363. Continue to the crossroads with the B3355 and turn left, heading northwards into Paulton. Pass the hospital, continue into Winterfield Road and entrance to the ground is on the right, shortly after bend in the road.

SHOLING FC

Founded: 1884
Former Names: Vosper Thornycroft FC, VT FC and a number of other earlier names
Nickname: 'The Boatmen'
Ground: VT Group Sports Ground, Portsmouth Road, Old Netley, Southampton   SO19 9PW
Record Attendance: 585 (vs Salisbury City, 2006/07)

Colours: Red and White striped shirts with Red shorts
Telephone Nº: (023) 8040-3829
Ground Capacity: 2,000
Seating Capacity: 150
Web Site: www.pitchero.com/clubs/vtfc

GENERAL INFORMATION
Car Parking: At the ground
Coach Parking: At the ground
Nearest Railway Station: Sholing (1½ miles)
Club Shop: None
Opening Times: –
Telephone Nº: –

GROUND INFORMATION
Away Supporters' Entrances & Sections:
No usual segregation

ADMISSION INFO (2010/2011 PRICES)
Adult Standing: £8.00
Adult Seating: £8.00
Senior Citizen/Child Standing: £2.00
Senior Citizen/Child Seating: £2.00
Note: Children are admitted free of charge when accompanied by a paying adult
Programme Price: £2.00

DISABLED INFORMATION
Wheelchairs: Accommodated
Helpers: Admitted
Prices: Normal prices apply for the disabled and helpers
Disabled Toilets: Available
Contact: (023) 8040-3829   (Bookings are not necessary)

Travelling Supporters' Information:
Routes: Exit the M27 at Junction 8 and take the 2nd exit at the roundabout into A3025 Hamble Lane. After around ½ mile, turn right into Portsmouth Road (still the A3025) and the ground is on the right hand side of the road after ½ mile.

STOURPORT SWIFTS FC

Founded: 1882
Former Names: None
Nickname: 'The Swifts'
Ground: Walshes Meadow, Harold Davies Drive, Stourport-on-Severn   DY13 0AA
Record Attendance: 2,000

Colours: Black and Gold striped shirts with Black shorts
Telephone Nº: (01299) 825188
Ground Capacity: 2,000
Seating Capacity: 250
Web Site: www.stourportswiftsfc.co.uk

GENERAL INFORMATION
Car Parking: At the ground
Coach Parking: At the ground
Nearest Railway Station: Hartlebury (3½ miles) or Kidderminster (4½ miles)
Club Shop: None
Opening Times: –
Telephone Nº: –

GROUND INFORMATION
Away Supporters' Entrances & Sections:
No usual segregation

ADMISSION INFO (2010/2011 PRICES)
Adult Standing: £7.00
Adult Seating: £7.00
Senior Citizen/Junior Standing: £3.00
Senior Citizen/Junior Seating: £3.00
Note: Under-12s are admitted free of charge when accompanied by a paying adult
Programme Price: £1.50

DISABLED INFORMATION
Wheelchairs: Accommodated
Helpers: Admitted
Prices: Normal prices apply for the disabled and helpers
Disabled Toilets: None
Contact: (01299) 825188   (Bookings are not necessary)

Travelling Supporters' Information:
Routes: Take the A451 from Kidderminster to Stourport and follow this road along the one-way system through the town centre (follow signposts for the Sports Centre). Cross over the River Severn Bridge, turn left into Harold Davies Drive and the Sports Centre is on the left. The football ground is located at the rear of the Sports Centre.

TAUNTON TOWN FC

Founded: 1947
Former Names: None
Nickname: 'The Peacocks'
Ground: Wordsworth Drive, Taunton   TA1 2HG
Record Attendance: 3,284 (1999)

Colours: Sky Blue shirts with Claret shorts
Telephone Nº: (01823) 278191
Fax Number: (01823) 278191
Ground Capacity: 2,500
Seating Capacity: 300
Web Site: www.tauntontown.com

GENERAL INFORMATION
Car Parking: At the ground
Coach Parking: At the ground
Nearest Railway Station: Taunton (1¼ miles)
Club Shop: None
Opening Times: –
Telephone Nº: –

GROUND INFORMATION
Away Supporters' Entrances & Sections:
No usual segregation

ADMISSION INFO (2010/2011 PRICES)
Adult Standing: £7.00
Adult Seating: £7.00
Senior Citizen Standing: £5.00
Senior Citizen Seating: £5.00
Under-16s Standing/Seating: £2.00
Programme Price: £1.50

DISABLED INFORMATION
Wheelchairs: Accommodated
Helpers: Admitted
Prices: Normal prices apply for the disabled. Helpers pay
concessionary prices
Disabled Toilets: Available
Contact: (01823) 278191   (Bookings are not necessary)

Travelling Supporters' Information:
Routes: Exit the M5 at Junction 25 and follow signs for Taunton Town Centre. Bear left at the first set of traffic lights then go straight on at the next set of traffic lights into Wordsworth Drive. The ground is on the left hand side of the road after approximately 200 yards.

THATCHAM TOWN FC

Unfortunately, no ground photograph
for Thatcham Town FC was available
at the time of going to press.

Founded: 1895
Former Names: None
Nickname: 'The Kingfishers'
Ground: Waterside Park, Crookham Hill, Thatcham, RG19 4PA
Record Attendance: 1,400

Colours: Blue and White striped shirts with Blue shorts
Telephone N°: (01635) 862016
Fax Number: (01635) 873934
Ground Capacity: 3,000
Seating Capacity: 300
Web Site: www.thatchamtownfc.co.uk

GENERAL INFORMATION

Car Parking: At the ground
Coach Parking: At the ground
Nearest Railway Station: Thatcham (¼ mile)
Club Shop: At the ground
Opening Times: Matchdays only
Telephone N°: –

GROUND INFORMATION

Away Supporters' Entrances & Sections:
No usual segregation

ADMISSION INFO (2010/2011 PRICES)

Adult Standing: £7.00
Adult Seating: £7.00
Senior Citizen Standing: £4.00
Senior Citizen Seating: £4.00
Under-16s Standing/Seating: £1.00
Programme Price: £1.50

DISABLED INFORMATION

Wheelchairs: Accommodated
Helpers: Admitted
Prices: Normal prices apply for the disabled and helpers
Disabled Toilets: Available
Contact: (01635) 862016 (Bookings are not necessary)

Travelling Supporters' Information:
Routes: Thatcham is situated on the A4 between Newbury and Reading. Take the A4 to Thatcham then head south along Pipers Way at the roundabout to the eastern side of Thatcham. At the bottom of Pipers Way, turn left at the roundabout into Station Road, cross the railway line and bear right where the road forks before turning off immediately on the left for the entrance to the ground.

WIMBORNE TOWN FC

Photo courtesy of seekerphoto.co.uk

Founded: 1878
Former Names: None
Nickname: 'The Magpies'
Ground: Cuthbury, Cowgrove Road,
Wimborne Minster   BH21 4EL
Record Attendance: 3,250

Colours: Black & White striped shirts with Black shorts
Telephone Nº: (01202) 884821
Fax Number: (01202) 888023
Ground Capacity: 3,250
Seating Capacity: 275
Web Site: www.wimbornefc.co.uk

GENERAL INFORMATION
Car Parking: At the ground
Coach Parking: At the ground
Nearest Railway Station: Hamworth (9½ miles)
Club Shop: At the ground
Opening Times: Matchdays only
Telephone Nº: (01202) 884821

GROUND INFORMATION
Away Supporters' Entrances & Sections:
No usual segregation

ADMISSION INFO (2010/2011 PRICES)
Adult Standing: £7.50
Adult Seating: £7.50
Senior Citizen Standing: £4.00
Senior Citizen Seating: £4.00
Under-16s Standing/Seating: Free of charge
Programme Price: £1.20

DISABLED INFORMATION
Wheelchairs: Accommodated
Helpers: Admitted
Prices: Normal prices apply for the disabled and helpers
Disabled Toilets: To become available during 2010/11
Contact: (01202) 884821   (Bookings are not necessary)

Travelling Supporters' Information:
Routes: The ground is located on the western outskirts of Wimborne Minster which is situated just to the north of the A31. Take the A31 to the junction with with A349 then head north on the B3073 passing over the River Stour into Poole Road. Continue along the B3073 into Rodway, turn left at the roundabout into Lewens Lane and left again into Park Lane. Follow the road around right into East Street (still the B3073) and continue into King Street before taking the second exit at the roundabout into Victoria Road (B3082). Continue along this road then turn left into Cowgrove Road. The entrance to the ground is on the left after a short distance.

YATE TOWN FC

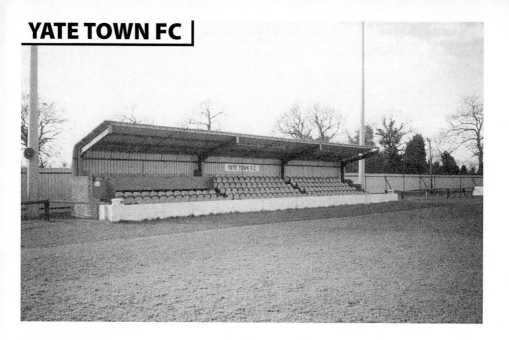

Founded: 1906 (Re-formed: 1946)
Former Names: Yate Rovers FC, Yate YMCA FC
Nickname: 'Bluebells'
Ground: Lodge Road, Yate   BS37 7LE
Record Attendance: 2,000
Pitch Size: 117 × 76 yards

Colours: White shirts with Navy Blue shorts
Telephone N°: (01454) 228103
Fax Number: (01454) 324305
Ground Capacity: 2,000
Seating Capacity: 250
Web site: www.yatetownfc.com

GENERAL INFORMATION
Car Parking: Large car park available at the ground
Coach Parking: At the ground
Nearest Railway Station: Yate
Nearest Bus Station: Bristol
Club Shop: At the ground
Opening Times: Matchdays only
Telephone N°: (01454) 324305 (Club secretary)

GROUND INFORMATION
Away Supporters' Entrances & Sections:
No usual segregation

ADMISSION INFO (2010/2011 PRICES)
Adult Standing: £7.00
Adult Seating: £7.00
Senior Citizen/Junior Standing: £4.00
Senior Citizen/Junior Seating: £4.00
Under-11s Standing/Seating: £1.00
Programme Price: £1.50

DISABLED INFORMATION
Wheelchairs: Accommodated
Helpers: One helper admitted per disabled fan
Prices: Free of charge for the disabled and helpers
Disabled Toilets: Available in the Clubhouse
Contact: (01454) 228103   (Bookings are not necessary)

Travelling Supporters' Information:
Routes: From the East: Exit the M4 at Junction 18 and enter Yate on the A432 via the Chipping Sodbury bypass. Turn right at the first roundabout (into Link Road), carry straight on over the next roundabout into Goose Green Way and over two more roundabouts and through two sets of traffic lights. At the third set of lights turn right then immediately left into Lodge Road. The ground is on the right after 200 yards; From the North/Midlands: Exit the M5 at Junction 14 and take the B4509/B4060 into Chipping Sodbury. Turn right into the High Street and continue down Bowling Hill then turn right at the first roundabout into Goose Green Way. Then as above.

Southern Football League Premier Division 2009/2010 Season	Banbury United	Bashley	Bedford Town	Brackley Town	Cambridge City	Chippenham Town	Clevedon Town	Didcot Town	Evesham United	Farnborough	Halesowen Town	Hednesford Town	Hemel Hempstead Town	Leamington	Merthyr Tydfil	Nuneaton Town	Oxford City	Rugby Town	Stourbridge	Swindon Supermarine	Tiverton Town	Truro City
Banbury United		1-1	0-0	0-3	1-0	0-0	4-3	1-0	0-1	0-3	2-1	3-2	1-1	1-2	3-1	2-1	1-1	2-1	3-3	3-1	0-1	0-0
Bashley	1-0		1-2	5-2	0-2	0-1	3-2	3-2	2-1	0-4	1-2	0-4	3-0	1-1	3-2	2-1	3-2	4-0	4-4	3-0	0-1	2-0
Bedford Town	1-1	0-4		2-2	0-2	1-2	3-1	1-5	1-2	2-2	1-1	3-2	5-0	0-2	2-4	2-1	1-1	3-1	0-1	1-2	2-0	0-2
Brackley Town	5-1	2-3	3-0		0-0	0-1	2-1	2-2	3-1	1-3	2-1	0-1	2-0	1-0	1-0	0-0	1-2	3-1	3-2	1-2	2-0	4-3
Cambridge City	2-1	2-2	4-2	5-0		1-0	4-1	4-1	1-1	1-1	1-1	0-3	1-1	2-2	1-1	1-1	2-0	1-0	6-1	5-0	1-1	0-3
Chippenham Town	5-0	1-2	3-0	2-3	2-1		2-0	2-0	2-1	2-0	1-1	0-1	6-1	4-2	1-5	2-1	2-0	1-0	2-2	0-1	4-2	2-1
Clevedon Town	1-2	0-2	0-3	0-3	0-1	0-0		1-1	1-4	1-4	3-3	0-3	1-0	1-3	1-1	0-3	1-2	1-3	4-1	2-6	0-1	0-3
Didcot Town	0-0	1-1	2-2	0-1	0-3	0-2	0-1		0-2	1-2	1-2	0-1	2-1	4-2	3-0	1-1	4-4	3-1	0-1	0-2	1-1	1-1
Evesham United	3-2	0-0	0-0	1-3	3-1	0-0	0-0	0-1		1-2	0-0	0-0	0-2	0-1	1-1	1-2	0-0	1-0	1-1	0-1	2-2	0-2
Farnborough	3-0	1-1	6-1	3-0	3-3	3-1	2-1	1-0	3-1		4-1	2-1	3-0	3-1	3-1	0-2	2-1	4-1	1-2	2-0	2-1	3-1
Halesowen Town	0-2	3-2	4-1	1-1	1-1	2-0	2-2	3-1	1-0	1-1		2-2	1-0	3-0	1-1	3-2	3-3	5-1	2-1	2-0	1-1	3-2
Hednesford Town	0-0	1-0	2-1	1-4	2-2	1-1	0-0	1-2	2-1	4-0	2-2		4-3	4-2	1-1	0-3	4-2	6-0	1-1	0-0	2-1	2-3
Hemel Hempstead Town	2-3	0-1	5-1	1-1	2-3	0-1	1-1	1-2	2-0	1-1	3-5	2-2		0-2	3-1	1-3	2-1	1-0	2-2	3-1	0-2	0-2
Leamington	3-3	0-1	2-0	2-1	1-0	4-4	0-1	3-5	4-1	2-3	2-2	1-3	3-1		5-3	0-2	1-2	2-1	2-1	3-1	5-0	1-3
Merthyr Tydfil	3-2	2-1	0-0	2-1	0-1	2-1	2-3	4-2	2-1	0-0	0-2	1-2	1-2	2-3		1-3	2-3	1-1	2-1	1-0	1-1	1-2
Nuneaton Town	5-0	5-2	4-0	2-2	1-1	0-1	4-2	2-0	2-0	1-1	1-1	3-1	3-1	1-1	3-1		3-1	1-1	0-0	1-0	1-0	4-0
Oxford City	1-1	1-1	4-1	2-3	0-1	0-0	1-2	1-1	3-0	1-1	2-2	2-0	2-2	1-1	2-2	1-4		3-0	1-3	2-1	1-0	2-2
Rugby Town	0-2	2-3	1-4	1-4	0-3	0-0	4-4	4-3	0-0	0-4	0-3	1-6	2-2	1-4	1-4	0-3	4-0		1-2	0-0	3-2	1-1
Stourbridge	2-1	2-2	2-0	4-2	3-1	1-0	4-1	1-0	0-0	3-2	1-4	1-1	2-0	2-1	2-0	1-2	0-2	6-0		0-0	2-1	7-2
Swindon Supermarine	1-2	3-3	0-0	1-7	1-1	1-1	3-2	1-1	1-1	0-7	1-2	0-0	1-0	2-3	1-1	2-4	2-4	5-1	2-2		2-1	0-4
Tiverton Town	2-1	0-5	2-0	1-1	0-0	0-0	0-0	1-2	0-1	0-2	0-2	0-2	0-0	2-3	0-1	1-2	1-0	3-1	2-2	0-0		1-2
Truro City	1-1	1-1	5-1	1-1	1-1	3-5	2-2	2-1	1-2	2-3	1-2	1-2	3-1	2-2	3-1	0-2	0-1	4-1	4-1	0-0	2-0	

Southern Football League Division One Midlands 2009/2010 Season	AFC Sudbury	Arlesey Town	Atherstone Town	Aylesbury United	Barton Rovers	Beaconsfield SYCOB	Bedworth United	Biggleswade Town	Bromsgrove Rovers	Burnham	Bury Town	Chesham United	Hitchin Town	Leighton Town	Marlow	Romulus	Rothwell Town	Slough Town	Soham Town Rangers	Stourport Swifts	Sutton Coldfield Town	Woodford United
AFC Sudbury	■	2-0	1-1	5-2	0-1	0-2	0-0	0-1	3-0	1-2	0-2	4-1	0-2	0-0	2-3	1-1	0-0	1-2	2-2	2-1	1-2	1-1
Arlesey Town	1-1	■	2-0	4-1	5-0	3-0	0-0	1-0	0-0	0-1	1-0	1-3	1-2	2-0	0-2	2-0	4-0	1-2	3-1	1-0	1-4	1-1
Atherstone Town	0-2	2-4	■	2-2	2-1	1-2	1-0	1-1	2-0	1-3	3-6	3-3	1-2	0-1	0-3	1-5	4-2	2-0	3-2	3-2	2-0	0-1
Aylesbury United	0-4	2-1	3-4	■	0-1	3-3	1-2	1-3	1-0	1-2	0-4	0-1	3-4	1-3	2-2	1-2	2-5	2-5	0-4	1-1	0-4	0-4
Barton Rovers	2-0	1-1	2-3	1-1	■	1-2	5-2	2-2	2-2	0-1	1-3	0-2	3-6	2-1	1-1	0-2	1-2	3-3	1-2	0-4	2-5	1-2
Beaconsfield SYCOB	0-0	1-2	4-0	1-2	2-5	■	4-0	0-2	2-2	1-4	1-2	1-4	1-1	2-0	1-0	1-4	0-1	1-4	0-4	0-6	0-2	0-2
Bedworth United	2-2	1-3	4-0	2-2	2-0	1-0	■	4-0	1-1	0-1	2-2	2-1	1-1	1-2	4-1	0-1	1-3	2-4	2-5	4-0	2-4	3-1
Biggleswade Town	0-0	3-2	1-0	3-1	2-1	1-1	1-0	■	1-1	2-1	0-3	1-1	0-3	1-0	2-3	0-1	0-4	1-0	1-0	2-2	3-3	3-1
Bromsgrove Rovers	2-3	1-2	1-1	5-0	1-0	3-1	1-1	1-1	■	2-2	0-4	0-0	0-1	0-4	2-0	2-2	1-0	1-1	0-2	2-1	0-1	1-2
Burnham	1-2	0-0	2-2	1-0	2-1	2-0	2-0	2-1	3-0	■	1-2	2-1	0-0	1-1	2-2	0-0	2-0	1-1	3-0	2-1	1-5	1-0
Bury Town	3-1	3-1	3-1	6-2	8-2	5-1	6-0	2-1	1-0	2-3	■	1-1	0-0	5-0	3-0	5-0	3-1	1-0	2-1	3-1	2-2	4-5
Chesham United	3-2	0-0	3-0	2-0	3-0	1-0	0-1	3-0	2-0	0-1	1-1	■	2-0	1-2	3-2	0-3	3-0	1-0	2-3	3-0	4-1	3-0
Hitchin Town	1-0	4-1	2-1	5-1	3-0	4-1	1-0	1-0	1-1	4-0	1-0	1-2	■	3-0	3-0	2-0	4-0	3-2	1-2	2-1	3-2	3-0
Leighton Town	6-4	2-1	1-1	2-1	3-0	1-1	2-0	3-1	1-2	3-0	0-2	2-1	2-2	■	1-2	1-0	2-1	0-1	4-4	2-1	1-2	2-4
Marlow	2-0	1-1	1-1	4-0	1-0	3-0	3-3	0-0	2-4	0-1	1-2	1-1	1-1	0-2	■	1-2	1-0	0-1	6-1	2-2	2-4	0-1
Romulus	0-1	0-0	1-2	5-0	0-0	7-1	2-0	1-1	2-1	0-1	1-2	0-1	2-3	4-0	0-0	■	1-1	1-4	1-0	0-0	2-3	0-0
Rothwell Town	1-0	1-0	2-3	5-0	2-2	2-2	0-1	0-7	2-0	1-2	0-0	1-2	0-1	0-1	3-3	1-3	■	1-3	4-2	0-3	0-3	0-0
Slough Town	0-1	1-2	3-3	5-1	5-1	3-1	2-0	4-2	3-2	0-2	0-1	1-3	0-1	3-1	1-1	2-2	4-1	■	2-0	3-2	2-2	1-0
Soham Town Rangers	0-1	2-0	1-3	5-1	3-2	2-3	2-2	3-2	0-0	1-1	0-3	1-4	3-2	2-1	2-1	0-0	4-2	0-2	■	1-0	0-1	4-4
Stourport Swifts	1-1	0-1	1-3	5-4	2-0	0-0	2-0	0-0	5-1	1-4	1-2	1-1	0-1	2-0	2-1	2-4	1-1	1-4	1-2	■	1-0	3-4
Sutton Coldfield Town	0-2	1-0	1-2	0-2	1-1	2-1	1-1	5-2	1-1	3-1	3-4	2-1	1-3	3-2	2-2	2-2	3-0	2-2	6-0	1-1	■	2-1
Woodford United	3-2	2-2	1-0	6-1	1-0	3-1	2-5	1-1	4-1	1-3	0-2	0-2	1-3	2-1	2-3	3-2	1-2	0-1	1-0	1-2	1-1	■

Southern Football League Division One South & West 2009/2010 Season	Abingdon United	AFC Hayes	AFC Totton	Andover	Bedfont Green	Bishop's Cleeve	Bracknell Town	Bridgwater Town	Cinderford Town	Cirencester Town	Frome Town	Gosport Borough	Hungerford Town	Mangotsfield United	North Leigh	Paulton Rovers	Taunton Town	Thatcham Town	Uxbridge	VT FC	Windsor & Eton	Yate Town
Abingdon United		2-1	0-4	4-1	2-0	1-1	4-0	0-0	1-1	0-1	0-5	0-1	1-4	3-2	3-1	0-1	3-0	2-0	7-4	1-0	0-2	1-2
AFC Hayes	1-2		0-2	3-1	1-1	4-2	7-1	0-2	4-3	1-6	2-3	0-1	0-4	0-5	4-6	0-1	1-5	1-2	0-4	2-1	1-2	1-4
AFC Totton	2-1	5-0		2-0	2-1	4-0	9-0	0-0	4-0	2-1	1-0	4-1	3-1	2-1	3-1	0-1	8-1	5-1	2-1	1-3	0-0	3-0
Andover	1-2	3-2	1-0		2-1	1-1	5-3	0-1	0-0	0-0	2-2	0-2	0-4	1-2	0-1	2-2	3-0	0-5	2-1	0-3	0-2	1-0
Bedfont Green	5-3	2-1	1-2	3-3		1-2	8-0	0-4	0-0	2-2	1-4	1-5	3-2	3-1	0-2	1-2	1-3	4-5	2-3	3-4	0-2	2-3
Bishop's Cleeve	2-2	3-1	1-4	2-2	0-3		1-0	2-1	2-2	0-1	0-2	2-2	4-1	3-2	5-2	1-2	1-1	1-0	4-2	0-1	2-0	2-2
Bracknell Town	0-2	0-7	1-2	0-3	0-1	0-4		2-5	2-7	0-4	2-3	2-3	0-2	0-3	0-9	0-3	2-1	2-6	1-3	2-0	1-5	0-4
Bridgwater Town	1-1	3-0	1-3	3-0	0-1	2-0	5-0		2-0	2-3	2-2	2-1	1-0	2-1	1-1	3-1	1-0	2-1	1-0	1-1	2-1	1-0
Cinderford Town	2-5	1-1	2-0	2-1	0-1	3-0	4-1	0-8		2-1	1-1	2-2	2-4	3-1	2-1	1-3	0-1	2-0	5-0	2-3	0-1	4-0
Cirencester Town	3-2	3-1	0-1	3-2	5-2	1-2	11-1	0-0	3-1		1-0	3-3	3-1	2-2	2-1	1-1	5-0	0-0	1-2	3-2	1-2	2-0
Frome Town	3-1	3-1	1-1	1-1	3-1	2-1	4-0	1-3	1-0	3-2		1-1	2-1	2-0	2-1	0-0	2-1	1-3	3-1	2-2	1-1	0-0
Gosport Borough	4-2	2-1	0-2	4-0	2-2	1-1	6-0	0-2	4-2	2-0	0-0		3-0	4-0	1-2	4-1	2-2	3-0	0-1	0-1	0-0	2-0
Hungerford Town	2-2	0-1	0-1	4-2	0-3	0-0	2-1	0-0	1-0	1-3	0-0	1-1		1-2	0-1	1-5	2-1	1-2	2-1	0-1	0-3	4-1
Mangotsfield United	0-2	1-0	1-2	4-3	3-2	2-2	9-0	2-2	3-1	0-3	2-0	3-0	0-2		3-1	1-2	4-0	1-0	1-0	0-1	0-4	1-0
North Leigh	1-1	1-1	0-2	3-1	1-4	1-3	8-0	0-4	4-2	2-1	4-0	5-1	2-0	2-3		3-1	2-0	3-1	1-1	2-2	0-3	2-0
Paulton Rovers	3-1	3-1	2-3	2-0	1-2	0-0	5-1	1-1	3-1	0-2	0-1	2-4	1-0	2-2	0-1		2-0	4-6	1-3	3-0	0-0	1-1
Taunton Town	4-0	1-1	3-3	2-2	2-2	2-1	2-1	0-2	1-0	0-4	0-3	1-0	0-0	0-3	3-1	0-2		2-3	3-2	0-4	0-1	0-1
Thatcham Town	4-0	5-2	1-2	1-3	1-1	0-2	5-0	1-4	1-0	1-1	1-1	2-3	2-1	0-1	2-2	0-1	2-1		3-1	1-3	0-0	3-1
Uxbridge	5-1	2-0	3-4	2-0	4-3	0-1	3-1	2-3	0-3	2-1	0-3	3-0	0-1	2-1	1-1	2-2	2-4	0-2		4-4	0-1	2-2
VT FC	7-0	5-0	0-3	2-2	4-0	3-1	4-1	0-2	2-2	0-0	3-0	2-1	3-1	3-1	2-0	2-4	2-1	2-0	2-0		0-3	3-2
Windsor & Eton	2-0	1-0	1-0	3-2	1-0	2-1	6-0	1-1	5-0	0-1	0-0	2-1	5-1	1-1	3-1	4-0	2-1	2-1	5-0	1-0		2-1
Yate Town	1-0	1-0	3-2	1-1	3-3	1-1	2-1	1-0	0-1	0-1	0-0	2-3	2-1	4-2	4-0	2-2	2-1	4-2	1-1	0-3	0-2	

Southern League Premier Division

Season 2009/2010

Farnborough	42	28	9	5	100	44	93
Nuneaton Town	42	26	10	6	91	37	88
Chippenham Town	42	21	11	10	67	43	74
Hednesford Town	42	20	13	9	79	51	73
Brackley Town	42	21	9	12	83	61	72
Cambridge City	42	18	17	7	73	44	71
Bashley	42	20	11	11	79	61	71
Halesowen Town	42	21	17	4	84	53	70
Stourbridge	42	19	13	10	80	65	70
Leamington	42	19	8	15	84	75	65
Truro City	42	17	11	14	78	65	62
Banbury United	42	14	13	15	53	67	55
Oxford City	42	13	15	14	63	66	54
Swindon Supermarine	42	10	14	18	48	76	44
Didcot Town	42	10	11	21	56	70	41
Evesham United	42	9	14	19	35	52	41
Merthyr Tydfil	42	12	11	19	62	72	37
Bedford Town	42	9	10	23	50	88	37
Tiverton Town	42	8	12	22	35	61	36
Hemel Hempstead Town	42	8	10	24	50	81	34
Clevedon Town	42	6	11	25	48	92	29
Rugby Town	42	4	8	30	41	114	20

Halesowen Town and Merthyr Tydfil both had 10 points deducted for entering administration.

Promotion Play-offs

Chippenham Town 2   Hednesford Town 0
Nuneaton Town 6   Brackley Town 0

Nuneaton Town 2   Chippenham Town .... 1 (aet)

Promoted: Farnborough and Nuneaton Town

Southern League
Division One Midlands

Season 2009/2010

Team	P	W	D	L	F	A	Pts
Bury Town	42	32	6	4	115	40	102
Hitchin Town	42	31	7	4	91	36	100
Burnham	42	26	9	7	67	43	87
Chesham United	42	24	8	10	76	41	80
Slough Town	42	23	8	11	87	54	77
Sutton Coldfield Town	42	22	11	9	93	61	77
Woodford United	42	18	8	16	70	68	62
Romulus	42	16	13	13	66	48	61
Arlesey Town	42	17	10	15	58	48	61
Leighton Town	42	18	6	18	63	66	60
Soham Town Rangers	42	17	7	18	73	80	58
Biggleswade Town	42	14	13	15	56	63	55
Atherstone Town	42	15	9	18	65	82	54
AFC Sudbury	42	13	12	17	55	54	51
Marlow	42	12	14	16	64	65	50
Bedworth United	42	12	11	19	59	72	47
Stourport Swifts	42	11	10	21	63	69	43
Rothwell Town	42	11	8	23	53	80	41
Beaconsfield SYCOB	42	8	8	26	46	96	32
Bromsgrove Rovers	42	8	15	19	45	68	29
Barton Rovers	42	6	9	27	49	95	27
Aylesbury United	42	4	6	32	48	133	18

Bromsgrove Rovers had 10 points deducted.
Rothwell Town resigned from the League at the end of the
season.

Promotion Play-offs

Hitchin Town 1   Slough Town 2
Burnham 0   Chesham United 1

Chesham United 4   Slough Town 0

Promoted: Bury Town and Chesham United

Southern League
Division One South & West

Season 2009/2010

Team	P	W	D	L	F	A	Pts
Windsor & Eton	42	31	8	3	84	20	101
AFC Totton	42	32	4	6	105	36	100
Bridgwater Town	42	26	11	5	83	30	89
VT	42	25	7	10	90	52	82
Cirencester Town	42	23	9	10	91	46	78
Frome Town	42	20	15	7	68	44	75
Paulton Rovers	42	20	10	12	73	58	70
Gosport Borough	42	19	10	13	80	59	66
Mangotsfield United	42	19	5	18	77	66	62
North Leigh	42	18	7	17	83	72	61
Bishops Cleeve	42	15	13	14	64	64	58
Thatcham Town	42	17	6	19	76	72	57
Yate Town	42	15	10	17	58	64	55
Abingdon United	42	15	7	20	65	84	52
Uxbridge	42	14	6	22	70	85	48
Cinderford Town	42	13	8	21	66	78	47
Hungerford Town	42	13	6	23	53	68	45
Bedfont Green	42	12	8	22	77	90	44
Taunton Town	42	11	7	24	50	85	40
Andover	42	9	11	22	54	85	38
AFC Hayes	42	7	4	31	55	105	25
Bracknell Town	42	2	0	40	29	187	6

Gosport Borough had 1 point deducted.

Promotion Play-offs

AFC Totton 2   Cirencester Town 3
Bridgwater Town 3   VT 0

Bridgwater Town 3   Cirencester Town ...... 4 (aet)

Promoted: Windsor & Eton and Cirencester Town

F.A. Trophy 2009/2010

Qualifying 1	AFC Hornchurch	2	Brentwood Town	1	
Qualifying 1	AFC Sudbury	3	Billericay Town	3	
Qualifying 1	AFC Totton	2	Woodford United	2	
Qualifying 1	Ashton United	1	FC United of Manchester	3	
Qualifying 1	Atherstone Town	1	Leigh Genesis	3	
Qualifying 1	Aveley	2	Carshalton Athletic	5	
Qualifying 1	Banbury United	2	Bridgwater Town	2	
Qualifying 1	Beaconsfield SYCOB	1	Bashley	4	
Qualifying 1	Biggleswade Town	2	Chipstead	2	
Qualifying 1	Billericay Town	2	AFC Sudbury	2	(aet)
	Billericay Town won on penalties				
Qualifying 1	Bognor Regis Town	3	Ashford Town	1	
Qualifying 1	Boston United	3	Chorley	2	
Qualifying 1	Bracknell Town	1	Thatcham Town	8	
Qualifying 1	Bradford Park Avenue	0	Clitheroe	1	
Qualifying 1	Brigg Town	3	Burscough	2	
Qualifying 1	Burnham	3	Cinderford Town	2	
Qualifying 1	Buxton	1	Hednesford Town	0	
Qualifying 1	Cammell Laird	0	Guiseley	3	
Qualifying 1	Canvey Island	1	Hitchin Town	2	
Qualifying 1	Chesham United	2	Oxford City	2	
Qualifying 1	Chippenham Town	3	Frome Town	1	
Qualifying 1	Chipstead	2	Biggleswade Town	2	(aet)
	Chipstead won on penalties				
Qualifying 1	Cirencester Town	1	Godalming Town	3	
Qualifying 1	Clevedon Town	2	Brackley Town	4	
Qualifying 1	Corinthian Casuals	0	Arlesey Town	3	
Qualifying 1	Cray Wanderers	1	Burgess Hill Town	2	
Qualifying 1	Croydon Athletic	2	Ashford Town (Middlesex)	1	
Qualifying 1	Didcot Town	0	Cambridge City	1	
Qualifying 1	Evesham United	1	Windsor & Eton	1	
Qualifying 1	FC Halifax Town	2	Romulus	0	
Qualifying 1	Frickley Athletic	2	Bamber Bridge	1	
Qualifying 1	Garforth Town	0	AFC Fylde	3	
Qualifying 1	Hastings United	1	Merstham	6	
Qualifying 1	Hemel Hempstead Town	0	Farnborough	1	
Qualifying 1	Hendon	2	Lowestoft Town	0	
Qualifying 1	Horsham	4	Barton Rovers	4	
Qualifying 1	Hungerford Town	4	Taunton Town	3	
Qualifying 1	Lancaster City	1	Chasetown	1	
Qualifying 1	Leamington	1	Stourbridge	2	
Qualifying 1	Leek Town	2	Kendal Town	1	
Qualifying 1	Leighton Town	0	Whyteleafe	3	
Qualifying 1	Marine	0	King's Lynn	1	
Qualifying 1	Matlock Town	2	Loughborough Dynamo	1	
Qualifying 1	Merthyr Tydfil	0	Marlow	0	
Qualifying 1	Metropolitan Police	0	Kingstonian	1	
Qualifying 1	North Ferriby United	1	Worksop Town	1	
Qualifying 1	Northwood	1	Abingdon United	0	

Qualifying 1	Nuneaton Town	1	Hucknall Town	1	
Qualifying 1	Ossett Town	1	Willenhall Town	2	
Qualifying 1	Radcliffe Borough	2	Quorn	2	
Qualifying 1	Ramsgate	3	Leatherhead	0	
Qualifying 1	Retford United	0	Nantwich Town	1	
Qualifying 1	Rugby Town	0	Gosport Borough	1	
Qualifying 1	Rushall Olympic	0	Carlton Town	1	
Qualifying 1	Salford City	3	Durham City	0	
Qualifying 1	Shepshed Dynamo	2	Harrogate Railway Athletic	1	
Qualifying 1	Sittingbourne	0	Dartford	1	
Qualifying 1	Skelmersdale United	5	Goole AFC	0	
Qualifying 1	Soham Town Rangers	2	Harrow Borough	2	
Qualifying 1	Spalding United	1	Mossley	3	
Qualifying 1	Stocksbridge Park Steels	1	Glapwell	2	
Qualifying 1	Sutton United	0	Tonbridge Angels	2	
Qualifying 1	Swindon Supermarine	2	Fleet Town	4	
Qualifying 1	Tiverton Town	0	Truro City	4	
Qualifying 1	Tooting & Mitcham United	3	Walton & Hersham	0	
Qualifying 1	Uxbridge	1	Slough Town	1	
Qualifying 1	VCD Athletic	0	Concord Rangers	1	
Qualifying 1	Waltham Abbey	0	Boreham Wood	2	
Qualifying 1	Waltham Forest	1	Maidstone United	1	
Qualifying 1	Ware	1	Enfield Town	3	
Qualifying 1	Wealdstone	3	Margate	1	
Qualifying 1	Whitby Town	5	Warrington Town	2	
Qualifying 1	Witton Albion	1	Sutton Coldfield Town	1	
Qualifying 1	Yate Town	2	Bedford Town	1	
Replay	Barton Rovers	4	Horsham	3	
Replay	Bridgwater Town	0	Banbury United	1	
Replay	Chasetown	1	Lancaster City	4	
Replay	Harrow Borough	5	Soham Town Rangers	1	
Replay	Hucknall Town	0	Nuneaton Town	3	
Replay	Maidstone United	1	Waltham Forest	0	
Replay	Marlow	4	Merthyr Tydfil	2	
Replay	Oxford City	2	Chesham United	0	
Replay	Quorn	6	Radcliffe Borough	3	
Replay	Slough Town	2	Uxbridge	0	
Replay	Sutton Coldfield Town	2	Witton Albion	3	(aet)
Replay	Windsor & Eton	0	Evesham United	2	
Replay	Woodford United	1	AFC Totton	4	
Replay	Worksop Town	4	North Ferriby United	4	(aet)
	North Ferriby United won on penalties				
Qualifying 2	AFC Fylde	2	Glapwell	1	
Qualifying 2	Arlesey Town	2	Oxford City	1	
Qualifying 2	Barton Rovers	2	Billericay Town	2	
Qualifying 2	Bashley	2	Marlow	1	
Qualifying 2	Bognor Regis Town	0	Maidstone United	2	
Qualifying 2	Boreham Wood	3	Slough Town	2	
Qualifying 2	Boston United	0	Quorn	0	
Qualifying 2	Brackley Town	1	Mossley	1	

Qualifying 2	Buxton	0	Stourbridge	1	
Qualifying 2	Cambridge City	0	Matlock Town	1	
Qualifying 2	Carlton Town	0	North Ferriby United	3	
Qualifying 2	Carshalton Athletic	3	AFC Totton	1	
Qualifying 2	Chippenham Town	4	Tooting & Mitcham United	1	
Qualifying 2	Concord Rangers	2	Enfield Town	0	
Qualifying 2	Croydon Athletic	1	Burnham	1	
Qualifying 2	Dartford	3	Chipstead	0	
Qualifying 2	Farnborough	5	Burgess Hill Town	2	
Qualifying 2	Fleet Town	0	Ramsgate	2	
Qualifying 2	Frickley Athletic	0	Guiseley	3	
Qualifying 2	Godalming Town	1	Banbury United	1	
Qualifying 2	Harrow Borough	2	Wealdstone	2	
Qualifying 2	Hitchin Town	3	Gosport Borough	1	
Qualifying 2	Kingstonian	4	Hendon	2	
Qualifying 2	Lancaster City	3	FC United of Manchester	3	
Qualifying 2	Leigh Genesis	4	Skelmersdale United	1	
Qualifying 2	Nantwich Town	4	Leek Town	1	
Qualifying 2	Northwood	0	Evesham United	0	
Qualifying 2	Salford City	5	Clitheroe	3	
Qualifying 2	Shepshed Dynamo	0	FC Halifax Town	5	
Qualifying 2	Tonbridge Angels	6	Merstham	1	
Qualifying 2	Truro City	4	Thatcham Town	1	
Qualifying 2	Whitby Town	0	King's Lynn	2	
Qualifying 2	Whyteleafe	1	AFC Hornchurch	1	
Qualifying 2	Willenhall Town	0	Nuneaton Town	6	
Qualifying 2	Witton Albion	4	Brigg Town	1	
Qualifying 2	Yate Town	1	Hungerford Town	1	
Replay	AFC Hornchurch	4	Whyteleafe	0	
Replay	Banbury United	1	Godalming Town	3	
Replay	Billericay Town	3	Barton Rovers	0	
Replay	Burnham	2	Croydon Athletic	1	
Replay	Evesham United	1	Northwood	2	
Replay	FC United of Manchester	1	Lancaster City	0	(aet)
Replay	Hungerford Town	3	Yate Town	0	
Replay	Mossley	3	Brackley Town	1	(aet)
Replay	Quorn	3	Boston United	2	
Replay	Wealdstone	2	Harrow Borough	1	
Qualifying 3	AFC Fylde	1	Hinckley United	1	
Qualifying 3	Bashley	2	Staines Town	1	
Qualifying 3	Billericay Town	0	Hitchin Town	0	
Qualifying 3	Blyth Spartans	2	Stafford Rangers	0	
Qualifying 3	Boreham Wood	1	Hungerford Town	0	
Qualifying 3	Bromley	0	Maidstone United	1	
Qualifying 3	Chelmsford City	4	AFC Hornchurch	4	
Qualifying 3	Corby Town	1	Alfreton Town	1	
Qualifying 3	Dover Athletic	3	Dartford	2	
Qualifying 3	Eastleigh	1	Lewes	1	
Qualifying 3	Eastwood Town	0	Nantwich Town	3	
Qualifying 3	FC United of Manchester	2	Harrogate Town	2	

Qualifying 3	Farnborough	3	Wealdstone	0	
Qualifying 3	Farsley Celtic	5	Droylsden	2	
Qualifying 3	Fleetwood Town	2	Northwich Victoria	0	
Qualifying 3	Godalming Town	0	Arlesey Town	3	
Qualifying 3	Guiseley	3	FC Halifax Town	1	
Qualifying 3	Hampton & Richmond Borough	3	Concord Rangers	2	
Qualifying 3	Hyde United	3	Nuneaton Town	3	
Qualifying 3	Ilkeston Town	1	Mossley	1	
Qualifying 3	King's Lynn	1	Salford City	0	
Qualifying 3	Kingstonian	0	Chippenham Town	2	
Qualifying 3	Leigh Genesis	0	Redditch United	1	
Qualifying 3	Maidenhead United	1	Bath City	0	
Qualifying 3	Newport County	2	Braintree Town	1	
Qualifying 3	North Ferriby United	2	Gainsborough Trinity	2	
Qualifying 3	Northwood	2	Basingstoke Town	1	
Qualifying 3	Quorn	2	Vauxhall Motors (Cheshire)	3	
Qualifying 3	Ramsgate	0	Bishop's Stortford	3	
Qualifying 3	Stalybridge Celtic	1	AFC Telford United	1	
Qualifying 3	Stourbridge	0	Southport	0	
Qualifying 3	Thurrock	1	Havant & Waterlooville	4	
Qualifying 3	Truro City	1	Gloucester City	0	
Qualifying 3	Welling United	3	Tonbridge Angels	2	
Qualifying 3	Weston Super Mare	1	Carshalton Athletic	1	
Qualifying 3	Weymouth	3	Dorchester Town	0	
Qualifying 3	Witton Albion	1	Matlock Town	1	
Qualifying 3	Woking	6	St Albans City	0	
Qualifying 3	Worcester City	2	Burnham	1	
Qualifying 3	Workington	1	Solihull Moors	1	
Replay	AFC Hornchurch	1	Chelmsford City	2	
Replay	AFC Telford United	1	Stalybridge Celtic	2	
Replay	Alfreton Town	1	Corby Town	2	(aet)
Replay	Carshalton Athletic	3	Weston Super Mare	1	
Replay	Gainsborough Trinity	3	North Ferriby United	3	(aet)
	Gainsborough Trinity won on penalties				
Replay	Hinckley United	7	AFC Fylde	3	
Replay	Hitchin Town	0	Billericay Town	1	
Replay	Lewes	1	Eastleigh	0	
Replay	Matlock Town	4	Witton Albion	3	(aet)
Replay	Mossley	0	Ilkeston Town	2	
Replay	Nuneaton Town	1	Hyde United	0	
Replay	Solihull Moors	2	Workington	4	
Replay	Southport	4	Stourbridge	2	
Round 1	AFC Wimbledon	2	Boreham Wood	1	
Round 1	Arlesey Town	1	Chippenham Town	1	
Round 1	Bashley	2	Crawley Town	3	
Round 1	Bishop's Stortford	1	Maidenhead United	2	
Round 1	Blyth Spartans	2	Ilkeston Town	0	
Round 1	Cambridge United	3	Luton Town	1	
Round 1	Carshalton Athletic	1	Northwood	1	
Round 1	Chelmsford City	2	Truro City	2	

Round 1	Chester City	0	Fleetwood Town	1
Round 1	Corby Town	2	Farsley Celtic	0
Round 1	Farnborough	1	Newport County	3
Round 1	Gateshead	1	Harrogate Town	1
Round 1	Guiseley	1	Redditch United	0
Round 1	Hampton & Richmond Borough	0	Lewes	0
Round 1	Havant & Waterlooville	2	Dover Athletic	3
Round 1	Hinckley United	0	York City	0
Round 1	Kettering Town	0	Barrow	1
Round 1	Maidstone United	0	Histon	3

Maidstone United progressed to Round 2 after Histon were disqualified for fielding an ineligible player.

Round 1	Mansfield Town	0	Tamworth	2
Round 1	Matlock Town	0	Kidderminster Harriers	2
Round 1	Nantwich Town	0	Stalybridge Celtic	3
Round 1	Oxford United	1	Hayes & Yeading United	0
Round 1	Rushden & Diamonds	1	Billericay Town	0
Round 1	Southport	2	Gainsborough Trinity	2
Round 1	Stevenage Borough	2	Ebbsfleet United	0
Round 1	Vauxhall Motors (Cheshire)	8	King's Lynn	0
Round 1	Welling United	0	Eastbourne Borough	1
Round 1	Weymouth	0	Salisbury City	1
Round 1	Woking	1	Forest Green Rovers	0
Round 1	Worcester City	3	Grays Athletic	1
Round 1	Workington	2	Nuneaton Town	1
Round 1	Wrexham	0	Altrincham	0
Replay	Altrincham	1	Wrexham	0
Replay	Chippenham Town	2	Arlesey Town	0
Replay	Gainsborough Trinity	1	Southport	0
Replay	Harrogate Town	0	Gateshead	2
Replay	Lewes	3	Hampton & Richmond Borough	1
Replay	Northwood	0	Carshalton Athletic	5
Replay	Truro City	0	Chelmsford City	1
Replay	York City	3	Hinckley United	1
Round 2	AFC Wimbledon	3	Altrincham	1
Round 2	Blyth Spartans	1	Guiseley	2
Round 2	Cambridge United	2	Eastbourne Borough	2
Round 2	Chelmsford City	2	Crawley Town	1
Round 2	Fleetwood Town	0	Dover Athletic	1
Round 2	Gainsborough Trinity	0	Tamworth	0
Round 2	Gateshead	1	Chippenham Town	0
Round 2	Kidderminster Harriers	3	Lewes	2
Round 2	Maidenhead United	0	Barrow	1
Round 2	Newport County	0	York City	0
Round 2	Oxford United	1	Woking	0
Round 2	Salisbury City	2	Maidstone United	0
Round 2	Stalybridge Celtic	1	Corby Town	2
Round 2	Stevenage Borough	6	Vauxhall Motors (Cheshire)	0
Round 2	Worcester City	1	Carshalton Athletic	1
Round 2	Workington	2	Rushden & Diamonds	1

Replay	Carshalton Athletic	0	Worcester City	4
Replay	Eastbourne Borough	0	Cambridge United	2
Replay	Tamworth	2	Gainsborough Trinity	1
Replay	York City	1	Newport County	0
Round 3	AFC Wimbledon	2	Workington	3
Round 3	Barrow	1	Gateshead	1
Round 3	Cambridge United	0	Salisbury City	0
Round 3	Chelmsford City	1	Oxford United	3
Round 3	Guiseley	0	Tamworth	1
Round 3	Stevenage Borough	4	Dover Athletic	1
Round 3	Worcester City	0	Kidderminster Harriers	1
Round 3	York City	1	Corby Town	0
Replay	Gateshead	2	Barrow	3
Replay	Salisbury City	2	Cambridge United	1
Round 4	Barrow	2	York City	1
Round 4	Oxford United	1	Kidderminster Harriers	2
Round 4	Salisbury City	2	Tamworth	1
Round 4	Stevenage Borough	2	Workington	1

Semi-finals

1st leg	Kidderminster Harriers	1	Stevenage Borough	5
2nd leg	Stevenage Borough	0	Kidderminster Harriers	0
	Stevenage Borough won 5-1 on aggregate			
1st leg	Salisbury City	0	Barrow	1
2nd leg	Barrow	2	Salisbury City	1
	Barrow won 3-1 on aggregate			
FINAL	Barrow	2	Stevenage Borough	1

85

F.A. Vase 2009/2010

Round 1	AFC Wulfrunians	1	Friar Lane & Epworth	5	
Round 1	Almondsbury Town	3	Melksham Town	1	
Round 1	Ardley United	0	Moneyfields	1	
Round 1	Armthorpe Welfare	3	Liversedge	1	
Round 1	Arnold Town	0	Long Eaton United	1	
Round 1	Ash United	3	Badshot Lea	4	(aet)
Round 1	Bartley Green	1	Newcastle Town	2	(aet)
Round 1	Bedfont	1	Shoreham	1	(aet)
Round 1	Bemerton Heath Harlequins	1	Alresford Town	1	(aet)
Round 1	Bewdley Town	2	Coleshill Town	1	
Round 1	Biddulph Victoria	2	Norton United	1	
Round 1	Biggleswade United	2	Kingsbury London Tigers	1	
Round 1	Blaby & Whetstone Athletic	3	Malvern Town	1	
Round 1	Blackstones	1	Lincoln Moorlands Railway	2	
Round 1	Bodmin Town	1	Saltash United	2	
Round 1	Borrowash Victoria	0	Gedling Town	4	
Round 1	Bottesford Town	0	Ollerton Town	1	
Round 1	Bourne Town	0	New Mills	1	
	A replay was ordered after New Mills were found to have fielded an ineligible player.				
Round 1	Bridlington Town	2	South Shields	0	
Round 1	Brislington	8	Porthleven	0	
Round 1	Bristol Manor Farm	2	Corsham Town	1	
Round 1	Broxbourne Borough V&E	1	Stotfold	2	
Round 1	Burnham Ramblers	1	Bedford	2	
Round 1	Cambridge Regional College	7	March Town United	1	
Round 1	Cheadle Town	2	Congleton Town	2	(aet)
Round 1	Clevedon United	3	Tavistock	5	
Round 1	Cockfosters	1	North Greenford United	2	
Round 1	Colne	0	Hallam	4	
Round 1	Consett	0	Bedlington Terriers	2	
Round 1	Crook Town	2	Northallerton Town	0	
Round 1	Daisy Hill	6	Worsbrough Bridge Athletic	2	
Round 1	Daventry Town	2	Rothwell Corinthians	0	
Round 1	Daventry United	2	Wellingborough Town	3	(aet)
Round 1	Dawlish Town	3	Liskeard Athletic	0	
Round 1	Dorking	0	Chertsey Town	2	
Round 1	Downton	2	Fareham Town	4	(aet)
Round 1	Dunkirk	2	Winterton Rangers	0	(aet)
Round 1	East Grinstead Town	0	Whitehawk	5	
Round 1	Eastbourne United	4	Greenwich Borough	3	(aet)
Round 1	Ely City	3	Eynesbury Rovers	2	
Round 1	Enfield 1893	1	Southend Manor	0	
Round 1	Epsom & Ewell	3	Farnborough North End	2	(aet)
Round 1	Erith & Belvedere	2	Pagham	1	
Round 1	Felixstowe & Walton United	1	Long Buckby	1	(aet)
Round 1	Grimsby Borough	1	Gresley	3	
Round 1	Guisborough Town	1	Norton & Stockton Ancients	2	
Round 1	Halstead Town	3	Dunstable Town	0	
Round 1	Haverhill Rovers	2	Bugbrooke St Michaels	3	

Round 1	Herne Bay	1	Hythe Town	0	
Round 1	Hillingdon Borough	1	Brimsdown Rovers	2	
Round 1	Kidlington	1	Bradford Town	2	
Round 1	Kirkley & Pakefield	3	Newmarket Town	1	
Round 1	Langford	1	Wembley	2	
Round 1	Laverstock & Ford	1	Brockenhurst	2	
Round 1	Leeds Carnegie	2	Shildon	3	
Round 1	Leverstock Green	0	Hadley	1	
Round 1	London Colney	2	Bethnal Green United	1	
Round 1	Longwell Green Sports	2	Wantage Town	1	
Round 1	Loughborough University	1	Causeway United	1	(aet)
Round 1	Louth Town	3	Sleaford Town	4	(aet)
Round 1	Mole Valley SCR	0	Beckenham Town	1	
Round 1	Molesey	1	Arundel	2	
Round 1	Nelson	2	Selby Town	0	
Round 1	Newcastle Benfield	1	Tow Law Town	0	
Round 1	Newport Pagnell Town	5	Erith Town	1	
Round 1	North Shields	2	Pickering Town	3	
Round 1	Northampton Spencer	0	Wroxham	3	
Round 1	Oldham Town	0	Winsford United	1	
Round 1	Padiham	4	Hemsworth MW	2	
Round 1	Peacehaven & Telscombe	3	Chichester City	1	
Round 1	Penrith	5	Dinnington Town	0	
Round 1	Plymouth Parkway	4	St Blazey	2	(aet)
Round 1	Poole Town	4	Bishop Sutton	1	
Round 1	Rainworth MW	2	Deeping Rangers	1	
Round 1	Ramsbottom United	2	Bacup Borough	4	(aet)
Round 1	Redhill	3	Camberley Town	1	(aet)
Round 1	Ringmer	2	Crowborough Athletic	3	
Round 1	Rossington Main	0	Alsager Town	3	
Round 1	Royston Town	5	Basildon United	3	
Round 1	Shortwood United	3	Winchester City	1	
Round 1	Shrivenham	0	Flackwell Heath	2	
Round 1	Southam United	1	Oadby Town	2	(aet)
Round 1	Stokesley SC	0	Morpeth Town	2	
Round 1	Studley	0	Boldmere St Michaels	1	
Round 1	Tipton Town	3	Kirby Muxloe	1	
Round 1	Tiptree United	1	Harefield United	0	(aet)
Round 1	Tividale	3	Wolverhampton Casuals	2	(aet)
Round 1	United Services Portsmouth	0	Hamble ASSC	1	
Round 1	Walsall Wood	0	Westfields	2	
Round 1	Wednesfield	0	Barwell	3	
Round 1	Wellington	4	Dosthill Colts	1	
Round 1	Wellington Town	3	Barnstaple Town	1	
Round 1	Wells City	3	Verwood Town	0	
Round 1	Welton Rovers	6	Keynsham Town	0	
Round 1	West Auckland Town	5	Hall Road Rangers	1	
Round 1	Westbury United	0	Carterton	1	
Round 1	Whickham	1	Tadcaster Albion	0	(aet)
Round 1	Whitton United	1	Woodbridge Town	3	
Round 1	Wick	1	Faversham Town	2	
Round 1	Willand Rovers	5	Newquay	2	

Round 1	Wimborne Town	6	Gillingham Town	1	
Round 1	Witham Town	1	Hoddesdon Town	2	
Round 1	Wivenhoe Town	1	Stansted	3	
Replay	Alresford Town	1	Bemerton Heath Harlequins	5	
Replay	Bourne Town	2	New Mills	2	(aet)
	New Mills won on penalties				
Replay	Causeway United	2	Loughborough University	1	
Replay	Congleton Town	5	Cheadle Town	2	
Replay	Long Buckby	5	Felixstowe & Walton United	1	
Replay	Shoreham	2	Bedfont	0	(aet)
Round 2	Arundel	4	Crowborough Athletic	0	
Round 2	Badshot Lea	2	Faversham Town	1	
Round 2	Barwell	2	Long Eaton United	0	
Round 2	Beckenham Town	2	Carterton	1	
Round 2	Bedlington Terriers	1	Spennymoor Town	5	
Round 2	Biddulph Victoria	1	Gedling Town	0	(aet)
Round 2	Bideford	0	Welton Rovers	2	
Round 2	Blaby & Whetstone Athletic	0	Boldmere St Michaels	1	
Round 2	Bootle	2	Stone Dominoes	1	
Round 2	Brimsdown Rovers	3	London Colney	2	
Round 2	Brislington	0	Poole Town	4	
Round 2	Bristol Manor Farm	2	Saltash United	1	
Round 2	Bugbrooke St Michaels	0	Leiston	4	
Round 2	Cambridge Regional College	4	Enfield 1893	1	
Round 2	Causeway United	3	Newcastle Town	2	
Round 2	Chalfont St Peter	1	Peacehaven & Telscombe	5	
Round 2	Chertsey Town	2	Croydon	0	
Round 2	Christchurch	2	Almondsbury Town	5	
Round 2	Coalville Town	4	Oadby Town	2	(aet)
Round 2	Congleton Town	0	Shildon	2	
Round 2	Crook Town	2	Bacup Borough	0	
Round 2	Daisy Hill	2	Armthorpe Welfare	3	(aet)
Round 2	Dawlish Town	3	Wimborne Town	1	
Round 2	Dunkirk	3	Lincoln Moorlands Railway	1	
Round 2	Eastbourne United	4	Hamble ASSC	2	
Round 2	Ely City	1	Woodbridge Town	1	(aet)
	Ely City progressed to Round 3 after Woodbridge Town were disqualified.				
Round 2	FC Clacton	0	St Ives Town	2	
Round 2	Friar Lane & Epworth	1	Tipton Town	2	
Round 2	Glossop North End	1	Dunston UTS	0	
Round 2	Gresley	3	Ollerton Town	1	
Round 2	Herne Bay	0	Flackwell Heath	1	
Round 2	Kirkley & Pakefield	2	Biggleswade United	0	
Round 2	Long Buckby	2	Stansted	1	
Round 2	Longwell Green Sports	2	Willand Rovers	3	(aet)
Round 2	Moneyfields	2	Epsom & Ewell	3	
Round 2	Needham Market	5	Bedford	0	
Round 2	Nelson	3	Morpeth Town	1	
Round 2	New Mills	6	Tividale	1	
Round 2	Newcastle Benfield	1	Marske United	2	

Round 2	Newport Pagnell Town	3	Dereham Town	1	
Round 2	North Greenford United	0	Daventry Town	1	
Round 2	Padiham	2	Norton & Stockton Ancients	4	
Round 2	Penrith	5	Hallam	2	
Round 2	Plymouth Parkway	3	Bitton	2	
Round 2	Redhill	1	Shoreham	2	
Round 2	Scarborough Athletic	2	Bridlington Town	5	
Round 2	Shortwood United	3	Bemerton Heath Harlequins	0	
Round 2	Sleaford Town	2	Bewdley Town	1	
Round 2	Stanway Rovers	1	Hadley	0	
Round 2	Stewarts & Lloyds	2	Stotfold	4	(aet)
Round 2	Tavistock	1	Brockenhurst	3	
Round 2	Tiptree United	4	Cogenhoe United	3	(aet)
Round 2	Wellingborough Town	0	Royston Town	4	
Round 2	Wellington	3	Stratford Town	0	
Round 2	Wellington Town	3	Bradford Town	2	
Round 2	Wells City	2	Larkhall Athletic	3	(aet)
Round 2	Wembley	1	Hoddesdon Town	2	
Round 2	West Auckland Town	4	Whickham	0	
Round 2	Westfields	1	Rainworth MW	2	
Round 2	Whitehawk	3	Fareham Town	2	(aet)
Round 2	Whitley Bay	2	Alsager Town	0	
Round 2	Winsford United	1	Pickering Town	2	
Round 2	Witney United	5	Erith & Belvedere	1	
Round 2	Wroxham	0	Halstead Town	0	(aet)
Replay	Halstead Town	1	Wroxham	3	
Round 3	Armthorpe Welfare	2	Bridlington Town	1	
Round 3	Barwell	2	Glossop North End	0	
Round 3	Biddulph Victoria	1	Causeway United	3	
Round 3	Brimsdown Rovers	3	Newport Pagnell Town	2	(aet)
Round 3	Cambridge Regional College	1	Needham Market	2	
Round 3	Chertsey Town	3	Sleaford Town	2	(aet)
Round 3	Coalville Town	0	Tipton Town	2	
Round 3	Crook Town	2	Shildon	4	
Round 3	Dawlish Town	3	Brockenhurst	1	(aet)
Round 3	Eastbourne United	3	Poole Town	5	(aet)
Round 3	Flackwell Heath	1	Wroxham	3	
Round 3	Gresley	1	Spennymoor Town	0	
Round 3	Hoddesdon Town	0	Kirkley & Pakefield	4	
Round 3	Larkhall Athletic	0	Whitehawk	2	
Round 3	Leiston	3	Daventry Town	4	(aet)
Round 3	Long Buckby	5	Wellington	2	
Round 3	Marske United	5	Nelson	0	
Round 3	New Mills	5	West Auckland Town	1	
Round 3	Peacehaven & Telscombe	0	Bristol Manor Farm	3	
Round 3	Penrith	1	Bootle	4	
Round 3	Pickering Town	1	Dunkirk	1	(aet)
Round 3	Plymouth Parkway	4	Arundel	2	(aet)
Round 3	Rainworth MW	1	Norton & Stockton Ancients	2	
Round 3	Royston Town	2	Stanway Rovers	1	

Round 3	Shortwood United	2	Shoreham	0	
Round 3	St Ives Town	3	Ely City	0	
Round 3	Stotfold	3	Badshot Lea	1	
Round 3	Tiptree United	3	Beckenham Town	2	
Round 3	Wellington Town	2	Epsom & Ewell	3	(aet)
Round 3	Whitley Bay	3	Boldmere St Michaels	1	
Round 3	Willand Rovers	6	Welton Rovers	1	
Round 3	Witney United	4	Almondsbury Town	0	
Replay	Dunkirk	2	Pickering Town	2	(aet)
	Pickering Town won on penalties				
Round 4	Armthorpe Welfare	1	Wroxham	1	(aet)
Round 4	Brimsdown Rovers	1	Daventry Town	4	
Round 4	Bristol Manor Farm	1	Whitehawk	3	
Round 4	Chertsey Town	6	Plymouth Parkway	0	
Round 4	Dawlish Town	4	Gresley	4	(aet)
Round 4	Long Buckby	3	Epsom & Ewell	2	
Round 4	Needham Market	5	Kirkley & Pakefield	3	
Round 4	New Mills	2	Witney United	1	
Round 4	Norton & Stockton Ancients	4	Bootle	2	
Round 4	Pickering Town	1	Marske United	2	
Round 4	Royston Town	2	Tipton Town	1	(aet)
Round 4	Shortwood United	0	Barwell	3	
Round 4	Stotfold	0	Shildon	2	
Round 4	Tiptree United	0	St Ives Town	7	
Round 4	Whitley Bay	3	Poole Town	1	
Round 4	Willand Rovers	2	Causeway United	0	
Replay	Gresley	1	Dawlish Town	1	(aet)
	Gresley won on penalties				
Replay	Wroxham	1	Armthorpe Welfare	1	(aet)
	Wroxham won on penalties				
Round 5	Chertsey Town	1	Whitley Bay	1	(aet)
Round 5	Long Buckby	3	Gresley	4	
Round 5	Needham Market	2	Daventry Town	0	
Round 5	New Mills	0	Norton & Stockton Ancients	2	
Round 5	Royston Town	0	Wroxham	5	
Round 5	St Ives Town	1	Shildon	3	(aet)
Round 5	Whitehawk	1	Marske United	1	(aet)
Round 5	Willand Rovers	2	Barwell	2	(aet)
Replay	Barwell	2	Willand Rovers	1	(aet)
Replay	Marske United	2	Whitehawk	3	
Replay	Whitley Bay	2	Chertsey Town	1	
Round 6	Barwell	3	Norton & Stockton Ancients	0	
Round 6	Gresley	1	Whitehawk	3	
Round 6	Needham Market	1	Wroxham	2	
Round 6	Shildon	1	Whitley Bay	5	

Semi-finals

1st leg	Barwell	3	Whitley Bay	3
2nd leg	Whitley Bay	3	Barwell	2
	Whitley Bay won 6-5 on aggregate			

1st leg	Whitehawk	0	Wroxham	2
2nd leg	Wroxham	2	Whitehawk	1
	Wroxham won 4-1 on aggregate			

FINAL	Whitley Bay	6	Wroxham	1

Zamaretto Southern Football League Premier Division 2010/2011 Fixtures	Banbury United	Bashley	Bedford Town	Brackley Town	Cambridge City	Chesham United	Chippenham Town	Cirencester Town	Didcot Town	Evesham United	Halesowen Town	Hednesford Town	Hemel Hempstead Town	Leamington	Oxford City	Salisbury City	Stourbridge	Swindon Supermarine	Tiverton Town	Truro City	Weymouth	Windsor & Eton
Banbury United	■	14/09	26/03	27/12	16/11	11/12	19/02	29/01	15/01	30/08	12/02	17/08	05/10	27/11	23/10	06/11	09/04	18/09	21/08	23/04	05/03	19/03
Bashley	18/12	■	08/01	09/04	06/11	05/10	04/09	04/12	21/08	23/10	19/03	26/02	26/03	29/01	22/02	17/08	02/10	20/11	25/04	12/02	03/01	28/08
Bedford Town	09/10	18/09	■	16/11	27/12	30/08	05/03	02/04	12/02	15/01	17/08	19/10	12/03	14/09	29/01	23/04	13/11	11/12	16/04	21/08	19/02	27/11
Brackley Town	25/04	19/10	22/02	■	14/08	05/02	24/08	08/01	20/11	04/12	26/02	02/10	22/01	02/04	03/01	09/10	28/08	16/04	13/11	12/03	18/12	04/09
Cambridge City	22/02	12/03	25/04	29/01	■	13/11	02/10	16/04	26/02	20/11	02/04	12/02	03/01	17/08	18/12	21/08	04/09	09/10	28/08	04/12	08/01	19/10
Chesham United	28/08	02/04	03/01	21/08	19/03	■	09/10	22/02	06/11	26/02	04/12	20/11	25/04	19/10	17/08	16/04	08/01	12/02	04/09	29/01	02/10	18/12
Chippenham Town	20/11	15/01	04/12	12/02	23/04	26/03	■	21/08	18/09	22/02	14/09	29/01	23/10	11/12	26/02	30/08	05/10	27/12	17/08	09/04	19/03	06/11
Cirencester Town	14/08	05/03	05/10	18/09	23/10	16/11	05/02	■	23/04	27/12	11/12	19/03	09/04	19/02	06/11	15/01	24/08	30/08	27/11	14/09	26/03	22/01
Didcot Town	04/09	05/02	24/08	19/02	27/11	12/03	08/01	02/10	■	14/08	16/04	28/08	18/12	09/10	25/04	05/03	22/01	19/10	02/04	13/11	16/11	03/01
Evesham United	03/01	16/04	05/09	05/03	19/02	27/11	16/11	25/04	29/01	■	21/08	02/04	02/10	12/03	08/01	19/10	18/12	13/11	13/02	17/08	28/08	09/10
Halesowen Town	24/08	13/11	22/01	27/11	05/10	05/03	18/12	28/08	23/10	05/02	■	25/04	04/09	16/11	09/04	19/02	03/01	12/03	02/10	26/03	14/08	08/01
Hednesford Town	22/01	27/11	09/04	23/04	24/08	19/02	14/08	13/11	11/12	05/10	27/12	■	05/02	30/08	26/03	18/09	16/11	14/09	12/03	15/01	23/10	05/03
Hemel Hempstead T.	02/04	09/10	06/11	17/08	30/08	27/12	16/04	19/10	14/09	23/04	15/01	21/08	■	12/02	19/03	11/12	19/02	29/01	05/03	18/09	27/11	16/11
Leamington	26/02	14/08	18/12	05/10	22/01	09/04	28/08	20/11	26/03	06/11	22/02	03/01	24/08	■	02/10	19/03	25/04	04/12	08/01	23/10	04/09	05/02
Oxford City	16/04	16/11	14/08	30/08	14/09	22/01	27/11	12/03	27/12	18/09	19/10	09/10	13/11	23/04	■	02/04	05/03	15/01	19/02	11/12	05/02	24/08
Salisbury City	12/03	22/01	02/10	26/03	05/02	23/10	03/01	04/09	04/12	09/04	20/11	08/01	28/08	13/11	05/10	■	14/08	26/02	18/12	22/02	24/08	25/04
Stourbridge	19/10	23/04	19/03	11/12	15/01	18/09	02/04	12/02	17/08	14/09	30/08	22/02	20/11	27/12	04/12	29/01	■	21/08	09/10	26/02	06/11	16/04
Swindon Super.	08/01	19/02	28/08	23/10	26/03	25/08	25/04	03/01	09/04	19/03	06/11	18/12	14/08	05/03	04/09	27/11	05/02	■	17/11	06/10	22/01	02/10
Tiverton Town	05/02	27/12	23/10	19/03	11/12	15/01	22/01	26/02	05/10	24/08	23/04	06/11	04/12	18/09	20/11	14/09	26/03	22/02	■	30/08	09/04	14/08
Truro City	02/10	24/08	05/02	06/11	05/03	14/08	19/10	18/12	19/03	22/01	09/10	04/09	08/01	16/04	28/08	16/11	27/11	27/12	02/04	03/01	■	25/04	19/02
Weymouth	04/12	30/08	20/11	16/09	18/09	23/04	13/11	09/10	24/02	11/12	29/01	16/04	26/02	15/01	21/08	12/02	12/03	19/08	21/10	27/12	■	02/04
Windsor & Eton	13/11	11/12	26/02	15/01	09/04	14/09	12/03	17/08	30/08	26/03	18/09	04/12	22/02	21/08	12/02	27/12	23/10	23/04	29/01	20/11	05/10	■

92

Zamaretto Southern Football League — Division One Central 2010/2011

	AFC Hayes	Arlesey Town	Ashford Town (Middx)	Atherstone Town	Aylesbury	Barton Rovers	Beaconsfield SYCOB	Bedfont Town	Bedworth United	Biggleswade Town	Burnham	Daventry Town	Hitchin Town	Leighton Town	Marlow	North Greenford United	Northwood	Rugby Town	Slough Town	Soham Town Rangers	Uxbridge	Woodford United
AFC Hayes	■	26/02	03/01	18/12	27/11	13/11	29/01	25/09	30/10	16/04	17/08	21/08	09/10	12/03	12/02	25/04	15/01	04/09	08/03	19/10	07/12	02/04
Arlesey Town	04/12	■	09/10	19/02	18/09	22/01	14/08	20/11	11/12	30/08	06/11	19/03	27/12	08/01	02/04	16/04	05/03	19/10	05/02	16/11	23/04	14/09
Ashford T. (Middx)	30/08	26/03	■	23/10	22/01	05/10	11/12	27/12	08/01	19/02	09/04	05/02	19/03	14/08	23/04	05/03	16/11	20/11	04/12	06/11	14/09	18/09
Atherstone Town	14/08	07/12	16/04	■	02/04	14/09	23/04	08/01	27/12	19/10	19/03	05/03	22/01	11/12	26/02	12/02	06/11	16/11	18/09	09/10	27/11	30/08
Aylesbury	05/02	29/01	25/09	05/10	■	27/12	16/11	19/02	14/09	14/08	26/03	09/04	04/12	30/08	11/12	06/11	23/10	05/03	20/11	19/03	08/01	23/04
Barton Rovers	19/03	25/09	02/04	15/01	25/04	■	06/11	04/12	19/02	20/11	05/03	03/01	16/11	29/01	09/10	21/08	04/09	05/02	18/12	17/08	19/10	16/04
Beaconsfield SYCOB	18/09	18/12	16/08	04/09	07/03	12/03	■	05/02	13/11	09/10	03/01	04/12	20/11	30/10	18/10	02/04	21/08	15/01	25/04	19/02	16/04	22/01
Bedfont Town	22/01	12/02	25/04	21/08	08/12	26/02	27/11	■	12/03	09/03	15/01	04/09	20/10	13/11	30/10	03/01	18/12	16/04	18/08	18/09	02/04	09/10
Bedworth United	05/03	17/08	21/08	25/04	15/01	07/12	19/03	06/11	■	02/04	18/12	16/11	18/09	27/11	16/04	26/02	22/01	03/01	09/10	04/09	12/02	19/10
Biggleswade Town	23/10	03/01	07/12	09/04	18/12	12/02	26/03	16/11	05/10	■	29/01	17/08	06/11	26/02	27/11	15/01	19/03	21/08	04/09	25/04	25/09	05/03
Burnham	11/12	12/03	19/10	13/11	09/10	30/10	30/08	14/09	14/08	18/09	■	20/11	16/04	23/04	27/12	22/01	05/02	19/02	02/04	04/12	08/03	08/01
Daventry Town	08/01	13/11	27/11	30/10	19/10	30/08	26/02	23/04	08/03	11/12	12/02	■	14/09	07/12	14/08	09/10	18/09	02/04	22/01	16/04	12/03	27/12
Hitchin Town	26/03	25/04	13/11	25/09	26/02	08/03	12/02	09/04	29/01	12/03	23/10	15/01	■	05/10	07/12	04/09	17/08	18/12	21/08	03/01	30/10	27/11
Leighton Town	06/11	21/08	18/12	17/08	03/01	18/09	05/03	19/03	05/02	04/12	04/09	19/02	02/04	■	22/01	19/10	20/11	25/04	16/04	15/01	09/10	16/11
Marlow	20/11	05/10	04/09	04/12	17/08	26/03	09/04	05/03	23/10	05/02	25/04	18/12	19/02	25/09	■	16/11	03/01	19/03	15/01	21/08	29/01	06/11
North Greenford Utd.	27/12	23/10	30/10	20/11	12/03	08/01	05/10	30/08	04/12	14/09	25/09	26/03	23/04	09/04	08/03	■	19/02	29/01	13/11	05/02	11/12	14/08
Northwood	14/09	30/10	08/03	12/03	16/04	23/04	08/01	14/08	25/09	13/11	27/11	29/01	11/12	12/02	30/08	07/12	■	09/10	19/10	02/04	27/12	26/02
Rugby Town	23/04	09/04	12/02	08/03	30/10	27/11	14/09	23/10	30/08	08/01	07/12	05/10	14/08	27/12	13/11	18/09	26/03	■	12/03	22/01	26/02	11/12
Slough Town	16/11	27/11	26/02	29/01	12/02	14/08	27/12	11/12	26/03	23/04	05/10	25/09	08/01	23/10	14/09	19/03	09/04	06/11	■	05/03	30/08	07/12
Soham Town Rang.	09/04	08/03	12/03	26/03	13/11	11/12	07/12	29/01	23/04	27/12	26/02	23/10	30/08	14/09	08/01	27/11	05/10	25/09	30/10	■	14/08	12/02
Uxbridge	19/02	04/09	15/01	05/02	21/08	09/04	23/10	05/10	20/11	22/01	16/11	06/11	05/03	26/03	18/09	17/08	25/04	04/12	03/01	18/12	■	19/03
Woodford United	05/10	15/01	29/01	03/01	04/09	23/10	25/09	26/03	09/04	30/10	21/08	25/04	05/02	08/03	12/03	18/12	04/12	17/08	19/02	20/11	13/11	■

Zamaretto Southern Football League — Division One South & West — 2010/2011 Fixtures

	AFC Totton	Abingdon United	Almondsbury Town	Andover	Bideford	Bishops Cleeve	Bridgwater Town	Bromsgrove Rovers	Cinderford Town	Clevedon Town	Frome Town	Gosport Borough	Hungerford Town	Mangotsfield United	North Leigh	Paulton Rovers	Sholing	Stourport Swifts	Taunton Town	Thatcham Town	Wimborne Town	Yate Town
AFC Totton	■	05/10	11/12	08/03	30/10	14/08	18/09	04/12	26/03	08/01	14/09	27/12	09/04	23/04	23/10	19/02	22/01	20/11	05/02	13/11	30/08	12/03
Abingdon United	02/04	■	02/10	19/02	09/10	12/03	18/12	08/03	21/08	22/01	30/10	13/11	25/04	04/12	17/08	16/04	19/10	15/01	20/11	03/01	18/09	04/09
Almondsbury Town	18/08	27/11	■	30/10	15/01	29/01	09/03	16/04	25/04	12/02	26/02	12/03	08/12	20/10	21/08	18/12	09/10	02/04	25/09	04/09	13/11	03/01
Andover	16/11	07/12	05/03	■	18/12	12/02	02/04	18/09	15/01	16/04	19/10	22/01	03/01	19/03	04/09	21/08	17/08	09/10	06/11	25/04	27/11	26/02
Bideford	05/03	26/03	14/09	14/08	■	23/10	22/01	08/01	05/02	27/12	11/12	23/04	19/03	19/02	20/11	16/11	06/11	04/12	30/08	18/09	09/04	05/10
Bishops Cleeve	18/12	06/11	18/09	20/11	16/04	■	20/10	02/04	19/02	17/11	09/10	05/02	15/01	05/03	25/04	04/09	21/08	03/01	19/03	04/12	22/01	18/08
Bridgwater Town	29/01	14/08	16/11	05/10	25/09	09/04	■	23/04	23/10	30/08	08/01	20/11	06/11	11/12	19/02	04/12	05/03	19/03	27/12	05/02	14/09	26/03
Bromsgrove Rovers	26/02	16/11	23/10	29/01	21/08	05/10	04/09	■	09/04	07/12	25/09	26/03	17/08	06/11	03/01	19/03	18/12	25/04	05/03	15/01	12/02	27/11
Cinderford Town	09/10	08/01	27/12	14/09	27/11	07/12	16/04	19/10	■	05/03	30/08	14/08	26/02	02/04	18/09	06/11	19/03	16/11	11/12	22/01	23/04	12/02
Clevedon Town	21/08	25/09	20/11	23/10	25/04	08/03	03/01	19/02	30/10	■	12/03	04/12	29/01	05/02	05/10	15/01	04/09	17/08	09/04	18/12	26/03	13/11
Frome Town	15/01	05/03	04/12	09/04	18/08	26/03	21/08	22/01	03/01	06/11	■	06/10	04/09	18/09	19/03	25/04	17/11	05/02	19/02	20/11	23/10	18/12
Gosport Borough	25/04	19/03	06/11	25/09	04/09	27/11	12/02	09/10	18/12	26/02	02/04	■	15/11	16/04	05/03	18/10	03/01	21/08	29/01	16/08	06/12	15/01
Hungerford Town	19/10	27/12	19/02	30/08	13/11	14/09	12/03	11/12	04/12	18/09	23/04	08/03	■	22/01	05/02	20/11	02/04	16/04	08/01	09/10	14/08	30/10
Mangotsfield United	04/09	26/02	09/04	13/11	06/12	30/10	16/08	12/03	04/10	27/11	29/01	23/10	25/09	■	15/01	03/01	12/02	14/08	26/03	21/08	07/03	25/04
North Leigh	16/04	11/12	08/01	23/04	12/02	27/12	07/12	30/08	29/01	02/04	13/11	30/10	27/11	14/09	■	09/10	26/02	19/10	14/08	08/03	12/03	25/09
Paulton Rovers	06/12	23/10	14/08	08/01	07/03	23/04	26/02	13/11	12/03	13/09	27/12	09/04	12/02	30/08	26/03	■	27/11	25/09	04/10	30/10	11/12	29/01
Sholing	25/09	09/04	26/03	11/12	12/03	08/01	30/10	14/08	13/11	23/04	08/03	30/08	05/10	20/11	04/12	05/02	■	29/01	14/09	19/02	27/12	23/10
Stourport Swifts	12/02	14/09	05/10	26/03	26/02	30/08	13/11	27/12	08/03	11/12	27/11	08/01	23/10	18/12	09/04	22/01	18/09	■	23/04	12/03	30/10	07/12
Taunton Town	27/11	12/02	22/01	12/03	03/01	13/11	25/04	30/10	17/08	19/10	07/12	18/09	21/08	09/10	18/12	02/04	15/01	04/09	■	16/04	26/02	08/03
Thatcham Town	19/03	30/08	23/04	27/12	29/01	26/02	27/11	14/09	25/09	14/08	12/02	11/12	26/03	08/01	16/11	05/03	07/12	06/11	23/10	■	05/10	09/04
Wimborne Town	03/01	29/01	19/03	05/02	19/10	25/09	15/01	20/11	04/09	09/10	16/04	19/02	18/12	16/11	06/11	17/08	25/04	05/03	04/12	02/04	■	21/08
Yate Town	06/11	23/04	30/08	04/12	02/04	11/12	09/10	05/02	20/11	19/03	14/08	14/09	05/03	27/12	22/01	18/09	16/04	19/02	16/11	19/10	08/01	■

ENGLAND INTERNATIONAL LINE-UPS AND STATISTICS 2009-2010

12th August 2009
v NETHERLANDS *Amsterdam*

R. Green	West Ham United
G. Johnson	Liverpool
A. Cole	Chelsea (sub. W. Bridge 84)
G. Barry	Manchester City (sub. M. Carrick 46)
R. Ferdinand	Manchester United
J. Terry	Chelsea
D. Beckham	L.A. Galaxy (sub. S. Wright-Phillips 46)
F. Lampard	Chelsea
E. Heskey	Aston Villa (sub. J. Defoe 46)
W. Rooney	Manchester United (sub. C. Cole 59)
A. Young	Aston Villa

Result 2-2   Defoe 2

5th September 2009
v SLOVENIA *Wembley*

R. Green	West Ham United
G. Johnson	Liverpool
A. Cole	Chelsea
S. Gerrard	Liverpool (sub. J. Milner 46)
M. Upson	West Ham United (sub. J. Lescott 64)
J. Terry	Chelsea
S. Wright-Phillips	Manchester City (sub. A. Lennon 46)
F. Lampard	Chelsea (sub. M. Carrick 46)
E. Heskey	Aston Villa (sub. J. Defoe)
W. Rooney	Manchester United (sub. C. Cole 80)
G. Barry	Manchester City

Result 2-1   Lampard, Defoe]

9th September 2009
v CROATIA (WCQ) *Wembley*

R. Green	West Ham United
G. Johnson	Liverpool
A. Cole	Chelsea
S. Gerrard	Liverpool (sub. J. Milner 81)
M. Upson	West Ham United
J. Terry	Chelsea
A. Lennon	Tottenham H. (sub. D. Beckham 80)
F. Lampard	Chelsea
E. Heskey	Aston Villa (sub. J. Defoe 60)
W. Rooney	Manchester United
G. Barry	Manchester City

Result 5-1   Lampard 2 (1 pen), Gerrard 2, Rooney

10th October 2009
v UKRAINE (WCQ) *Dnipropetrovsk*

R. Green	West Ham United
G. Johnson	Liverpool
A. Cole	Chelsea
S. Gerrard	Liverpool (sub. J. Milner)
R. Ferdinand	Manchester United
J. Terry	Chelsea
A Lennon	Tottenham H. (sub. D. James 15)
F. Lampard	Chelsea
E. Heskey	Aston Villa (sub. C. Cole 72)
W. Rooney	Manchester United
M. Carrick	Manchester United

Result 0-1

14th November 2009
v BRAZIL *Doha*

B. Foster	Manchester United
W. Brown	Manchester United
W. Bridge	Manchester City
G. Barry	Man. City (sub. T. Huddlestone 82)
M. Upson	West Ham United
J. Lescott	Manchester City
S. Wright-Phillips	Manchester City (sub. P. Crouch 82)
J. Jenas	Tottenham Hotspur
D. Bent	Sunderland (sub. J. Defoe 54)
W. Rooney	Manchester United
J. Milner	Aston Villa (sub. A. Young 87)

Result 0-1

3rd March 2010
v EGYPT *Wembley*

R. Green	West Ham United
W. Brown	Manchester United
L. Baines	Everton
S. Gerrard	Liverpool (sub. J. Milner 73)
M. Upson	West Ham United
J. Terry	Chelsea
T. Walcott	Arsenal (sub. S. Wright-Phillips 57)
F. Lampard	Chelsea (sub. M. Carrick 46)
J. Defoe	Tottenham H. (sub. P. Crouch 46)
W. Rooney	Manchester United (sub. C. Cole 86)
G. Barry	Manchester City

Result 3-1   Crouch 2, Wright-Phillips

24th May 2010
v MEXICO *Wembley*

R. Green	West Ham United (sub. J. Hart 46)
G. Johnson	Liverpool
L. Baines	Everton
S. Gerrard	Liverpool
R. Ferdinand	Man. United (sub. J. Carragher 46)
L. King	Tottenham Hotspur
T. Walcott	Arsenal (sub. A. Lennon 77)
M. Carrick	Man. United (sub. T. Huddlestone 62)
P. Crouch	Tottenham Hotspur (sub. J. Defoe 46)
W. Rooney	Manchester United
J. Milner	Aston Villa (sub. A. Johnson 85)

Result 3-1   King, Crouch, G. Johnson

30th May 2010
v JAPAN *Graz*

D. James	Portsmouth (sub. J. Hart 46)
G. Johnson	Liverpool (sub. J. Carragher 46)
A. Cole	Chelsea
T. Huddlestone	Tottenham H. (sub. S. Gerrard 46)
R. Ferdinand	Manchester United
J. Terry	Chelsea
T. Walcott	Arsenal (sub. S. Wright-Phillips 46)
F. Lampard	Chelsea
D. Bent	Sunderland (sub. J. Cole 46)
W. Rooney	Manchester United
A. Lennon	Tottenham H. (sub. E. Heskey 76)

Result 2-1   Tanaka (og), Nakazawa (og)

12th June 2010
v U.S.A. (WCF) *Rustenburg*

R. Green	West Ham United
G. Johnson	Liverpool
A. Cole	Chelsea
S. Gerrard	Liverpool
L. King	Tottenham H. (sub. J. Carragher 46)
J. Terry	Chelsea
A. Lennon	Tottenham Hotspur
F. Lampard	Chelsea
E. Heskey	Aston Villa (sub. P. Crouch 79)
W. Rooney	Manchester United
J. Milner	Aston Villa (sub. S. Wright-Phillips 31)

Result 1-1   Gerrard

18th June 2010
v ALGERIA (WCF) *Cape Town*

D. James	Portsmouth
G. Johnson	Liverpool
A. Cole	Chelsea
S. Gerrard	Liverpool
J. Carragher	Liverpool
J. Terry	Chelsea
A. Lennon	Tottenham H. (sub. S. Wright-Phillips 63)
F. Lampard	Chelsea
E. Heskey	Aston Villa (sub. J. Defoe 74)
W. Rooney	Manchester United
G. Barry	Manchester City (sub. P. Crouch 84)

Result 0-0

23rd June 2010
v SLOVAKIA (WCF) *Port Elizabeth*

D. James	Portsmouth
G. Johnson	Liverpool
A. Cole	Chelsea
S. Gerrard	Liverpool
M. Upson	West Ham United
J. Terry	Chelsea
J. Milner	Aston Villa
F. Lampard	Chelsea
J. Defoe	Tottenham H. (sub. E. Heskey 86)
W. Rooney	Manchester United (sub. J. Cole 72)
G. Barry	Manchester City

Result 1-0   Defoe

27th June 2010
v GERMANY (WCF) *Bloemfontein*

D. James	Portsmouth
G. Johnson	Liverpool (sub. S. Wright-Phillips 87)
A. Cole	Chelsea
S. Gerrard	Liverpool
M. Upson	West Ham United
J. Terry	Chelsea
J. Milner	Aston Villa (sub. J. Cole 63)
F. Lampard	Chelsea
J. Defoe	Tottenham H. (sub. E. Heskey 71)
W. Rooney	Manchester United
G. Barry	Manchester City

Result 1-4   Upson

ENGLISH FOOTBALL LEAGUE
& F. A. PREMIER LEAGUE TABLES
1888 - 2010

978-1-86223-203-7

NON-LEAGUE FOOTBALL TABLES
1889 - 2010

978-1-86223-204-4

AVAILABLE FROM WWW.SUPPORTERSGUIDES.COM

NON-LEAGUE FOOTBALL TABLES
1889 - 2008

978-1-86223-171-9

Football League Tables & Non-League Football Tables

NON-LEAGUE FOOTBALL TABLES
1889 - 2007

978-1-86223-162-7

ALL NON LEAGUE FOOTBALL TABLES BOOKS FEATURE THE FOLLOWING LEAGUES :

- Isthmian League
- Football Alliance
- Southern League
- Football Conference
- Northern Premier League

ADDITONAL LEAGUES FEATURED :

A
- Sussex County League
- The Essex Senior League
- The Northern Counties East League
- The Central League
- The Midland Combination

B
- The North West Counties League
- The Manchester League
- The Norfolk & Suffolk League
- The Warwickshire Combination

B
- The Wessex League
- The Corinthian League
- The Delphian League
- The Midland Alliance
- The Derbyshire Senior League
- The Notts & District League
- The Notts & Derbyshire League
- The Central Alliance

C
- Hellenic League
- Midland Combination
- Devon County League

Supporters' Guides Series

This top-selling series has been published since 1982 and the new editions contain the 2009/2010 Season's results and tables, Directions, Photographs, Telephone numbers, Parking information, Admission details, Disabled information and much more.

THE SUPPORTERS' GUIDE TO PREMIER & FOOTBALL LEAGUE CLUBS 2011

This 27th edition covers all 92 Premiership and Football League clubs. *Price £6.99*

NON-LEAGUE SUPPORTERS' GUIDE AND YEARBOOK 2011

This 19th edition covers all 68 clubs in Step 1 & Step 2 of Non-League football – the Football Conference National, Conference North and Conference South. *Price £6.99*

SCOTTISH FOOTBALL SUPPORTERS' GUIDE AND YEARBOOK 2011

The 18th edition featuring all Scottish Premier League, Scottish League and Highland League clubs. *Price £6.99*

RYMAN FOOTBALL LEAGUE SUPPORTERS' GUIDE AND YEARBOOK 2011

This new book features the 67 clubs which make up the 3 divisions of the Isthmian League, sponsored by Ryman. *Price £6.99*

ZAMARETTO SOUTHERN FOOTBALL LEAGUE SUPPORTERS' GUIDE AND YEARBOOK 2011

This new book features the 66 clubs which make up the 3 divisions of the Southern League, sponsored by Zamaretto. *Price £6.99*

EVO-STIK SUPPORTERS' GUIDE AND YEARBOOK 2011

This new book features the 67 clubs which make up the 3 divisions of the Northern Premier League, sponsored by Evo-Stik. *Price £6.99*

THE SUPPORTERS' GUIDE TO WELSH FOOTBALL 2011

The enlarged 12th edition covers the 112+ clubs which make up the top 3 tiers of Welsh Football. *Price £8.99*

These books are available UK & Surface post free from –

Soccer Books Limited (Dept. SBL)
72 St. Peter's Avenue
Cleethorpes, DN35 8HU
United Kingdom